Indiana ROCKS!

A Guide to Geologic Sites in the Hoosier State

Indiana ROCKS!

A Guide to Geologic Sites in the Hoosier State

INDIANA GEOLOGICAL AND WATER SURVEY

2018
Mountain Press Publishing Company
Missoula, Montana

GEOLOGY ROCKS!

A state-by-state series that introduces readers to some of the most compelling and accessible geologic sites in each state.

First Printing, October 2018
Second Printing, May 2023

Photos and maps by Indiana Geological and Water Survey unless otherwise credited.

Cover photo: Water cascades over the Ste. Genevieve Limestone at Upper Falls.

Library of Congress Cataloging-in-Publication Data

Names: Indiana. Geological and Water Survey.
Title: Indiana rocks! : a guide to geologic sites in the Hoosier state /
  Indiana Geological and Water Survey.
Description: Missoula, Montana : Mountain Press Publishing Company, 2018. |
  Series: Geology rocks series | Includes bibliographical references and
  index.
Identifiers: LCCN 2018041187 | ISBN 9780878426874 (pbk. : alk. paper)
Subjects: LCSH: Geology—Indiana—Guidebooks. | Indiana—Guidebooks.
Classification: LCC QE109 .I54 2018 | DDC 557.72—dc23
LC record available at https://lccn.loc.gov/2018041187

PRINTED IN THE UNITED STATES

P.O. Box 2399 • Missoula, MT 59806 • 406-728-1900
800-234-5308 • info@mtnpress.com
www.mountain-press.com

PREFACE

As the Education Outreach Coordinator for the Indiana Geological and Water Survey, I have the opportunity to travel through knobby hills, entrenched valleys, and wide open plains in order to meet and work with people in the farthest reaches of the state. Inevitably, enough time in the car seems to lead to the 1970s classic "Love the One You're With" playing on the radio. While the song is about finding contentment with one's relationships in life, I like to think of it as a happy reminder to love the *rocks* you're with.

There is a lot to love about Indiana geology. From the mountains of sand along Lake Michigan's azure waters to the fossiliferous banks of limestone breaking along the Ohio River, Indiana's wild, scenic landscapes have attracted scientists and artists for nearly 200 years. Textbooks typically cite the spectacular—the Grand Canyon, Giants Causeway, Antelope Canyon—and omit the interesting sites that occur in our own backyards. Nonetheless, great geology does not just happen in faraway places—it is all around us and influences practically every aspect of modern life.

If, like me, you've spent countless hours looking out of car windows and marveling at how landscapes change and grow, this book is for you. Earth processes occur all over the globe, and each place has a unique story to tell. So get outside, love the rocks you're with, and explore the geological foundations of the place you call home.

—POLLY ROOT STURGEON,
Indiana Geological and Water Survey

We dedicate *Indiana Rocks!* to
Richard L. Powell (left) and Henry H. Gray (right),
two pioneers in Indiana geology without
whom this work would not be possible.

ACKNOWLEDGMENTS

This book is a collaborative effort by the dedicated staff of the Indiana Geological and Water Survey: Polly R. Sturgeon, Education Outreach Coordinator; Deborah A. DeChurch, Editor; Matthew R. Johnson, Cartographer; Barbara T. Hill, Photographer; John M. Day, Photographer; and Todd A. Thompson, Director and State Geologist.

Field work and site assistance by Kimberly J. Cook, Shalom G. Drummond, and Christopher J. Sturgeon.

We appreciated the comments of the reviewers: Lee J. Florea, Samuel S. Frushour, Nancy R. Hasenmueller, Edward W. Herrmann, Brian T. Keith, Henry M. Loope, Patrick I. McLaughlin, Gary J. Motz, Richard L. Powell, and Todd A. Thompson.

Sincere thanks to Patrick Burns and Gary Roberson at Indiana Caverns, Jennifer Carey at Mountain Press Publishing, Rick Conwell at the Tippecanoe Battlefield Interpretive Center, Peggy Fisherkeller at the Indiana State Museum, Alan Goldstein at Falls of the Ohio State Park, Jon Havens at Irving Materials Inc., Ginger Murphy at the Indiana Department of Natural Resources, and Wyatt Williams at Spring Mill State Park for their help and feedback.

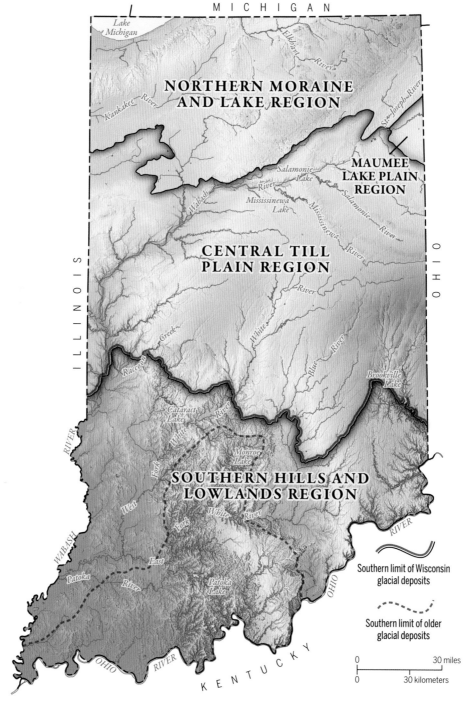

MICHIGAN

Lake Michigan

NORTHERN MORAINE AND LAKE REGION

ILLINOIS

Kankakee River

Elkhart River

St. Joseph River

OHIO

Salamonie Lake

Wabash River

MAUMEE LAKE PLAIN REGION

Mississinewa Lake

Salamonie River

Mississinewa River

CENTRAL TILL PLAIN REGION

River

Creek

White River

Raccoon Creek

Blue River

Brookville Lake

Cataract Lake

River

Monroe Lake

White Fork River

SOUTHERN HILLS AND LOWLANDS REGION

West Fork

White River

RIVER

RIVER

WABASH

Patoka River

East

Patoka Lake

OHIO RIVER

Southern limit of Wisconsin glacial deposits

Southern limit of older glacial deposits

| 0 | 30 miles |
| 0 | 30 kilometers |

OHIO RIVER

KENTUCKY

The fifty sites in this book are organized into three chapters according to physiographic regions.

CONTENTS

ERA	PERIOD	EPOCH	AGE	IMPORTANT GEOLOGIC EVENTS IN INDIANA
CENOZOIC	QUATERNARY	HOLOCENE	0.1	Glaciers have retreated from Indiana; weathering and erosion shape the landscape.
		PLEISTOCENE	2.6	Ice age; up to three-fifths of Indiana covered by glacial ice of the Laurentide Ice Sheet.
	NEOGENE		23	The Age of Mammals. Streams become entrenched after a series of tectonic uplifts; karst topography begins to form. Indiana moves into present location by 10 million years ago.
	PALEOGENE		66	
MESOZOIC	CRETACEOUS		145	Indiana located north of the equator and is above sea level. Long period of erosion leaves no rock record.
	JURASSIC		201	
	TRIASSIC		252	
PALEOZOIC	PERMIAN		299	
	PENNSYLVANIAN		323	Indiana located near the equator. Large rivers flow across state; swamp forests deposit carbon-rich sediments that become the origins of Indiana's coal.
	MISSISSIPPIAN		359	The Age of Crinoids. Indiana located south of the equator; carbonate shoals produce thick units of limestone. Influx of sediments from the Acadian Orogeny produces alternating layers of sedimentary rock.
	DEVONIAN		419	The Age of Fishes. Indiana located south of the equator. Extensive carbonates produced. Eroded sediments from the Acadian Orogeny carried into Indiana.
	SILURIAN		444	Indiana located south of the equator. Rise in sea level produces thick units of limestone and dolostone; extensive reefs flourish in southwest and northeast.
	ORDOVICIAN		485	Indiana located south of the equator. Shallow seas advance and retreat, depositing alternating layers of sedimentary rock. Nonnative invertebrates migrate into southeastern Indiana during the Richmondian Invasion.
	CAMBRIAN		541	Volcanic activity, plate tectonics, and sedimentation form earliest rocks. (Basement rocks are not exposed at the surface in Indiana and are known only by deep geologic drilling.)
PRECAMBRIAN ERA			4,600	

MILLIONS OF YEARS AGO

A Brief History of Indiana Geology

Indiana's rocks and sediments record a long and varied history of sea level rise and fall, distant mountain building and upland erosion, the development of reefs, shoals, and marshes, and the advance and retreat of continental-scale glaciers. It is no surprise then that Indiana contains just about every type of sedimentary rock and a variety of unconsolidated sediments. These rocks and sediments, however, accumulated across a vast time scale that includes a gap in the rock record of nearly 300 million years between Paleozoic rocks and Quaternary sediments.

The oldest rocks observable at the Earth's surface in Indiana are about 450 million years old and were deposited during the Ordovician Period. They occur in the southeastern part of the state and are exposed in the core of a domed and eroded area of rock that extends from Cincinnati north and northwestward past Chicago. Called the Cincinnati Arch (and, in part, the Kankakee Arch), it plunges to the northwest and divides two large-scale basins. These downwarped areas of sediment accumulation are known as the Michigan Basin in the north and the Illinois Basin to the southwest. Indiana occupies the margins of these two basins; therefore, the thickness of Indiana's sedimentary rock sequence is thinner than the package of rocks in the center of each basin.

The basins are part of the tectonic history of North America associated with the movement and interaction of continental plates that changed sea level, produced mountains, and warped the continent. For much of Indiana's bedrock history during the Paleozoic, what would become the North American continent was in the southern hemisphere—just south of or near the equator. The ocean flooded the middle part of this continent. During times of mountain building caused by plate collision along what is now the eastern edge of North America, the Appalachian Mountains and equivalent parts of Canada became upland areas. These highlands eroded, dumping large quantities of sediment onto the continent to accumulate as sandstone, siltstone, and shale. At other times when these siliciclastic sediments were not being introduced into the inland sea, carbonate rocks accumulated, primarily limestone and clayey (argillaceous) limestone. Other factors—the changing climate at worldwide and regional scales, the evolution of marine invertebrate organisms, and the development of land plants—also had significant influences on Indiana's bedrock geology. Of particular importance were the development of Silurian Period reefs, Mississippian Period shoals, and Pennsylvanian Period peat swamps.

As sediments accumulated, compacted, and cemented to become rocks, geothermally heated and mineral-rich water migrated up from deep in the basins and through the sediments, causing many limestones to be altered into magnesium-rich dolostones. The fluid also silicified parts of the limestones to create chert. In other sediments, organic material, such as microscopic plants and animals, was altered by the pressure and heat of burial to become fossil fuels—Indiana's petroleum and natural gas. Similarly, sediments consisting of terrestrial plants were transformed into coal.

In the stratigraphic column of the Ordovician to Pennsylvanian rocks exposed along Indiana's bedrock surface, the oldest and deepest rocks are fossiliferous limestone, argillaceous limestone, and calcareous shale. Many of these rocks are known for their inclusion of brachiopods and rugose corals. For the

BEDROCK GEOLOGIC MAP OF INDIANA

Pennsylvanian

Mattoon, Bond, Patoka, and
Shelburn Formations
Mostly shale and sandstone; some limestone and coal

Carbondale Group
Mostly shale and sandstone; some limestone and coal

Raccoon Creek Group
*Mostly shale and sandstone; thin beds
of limestone, clay, and coal*

Mississippian

Buffalo Wallow, Stephensport,
and West Baden Groups
Mostly shale and sandstone; some limestone

Blue River and Sanders Groups
Limestone; some gypsum

Borden Group
Mostly siltstone; some limestone and dolomite

Mississippian - Devonian

Coldwater, New Albany, Ellsworth, and Antrim Shales
Shale

Devonian - Silurian

Muscatatuck Group, Wabash and
Pleasant Mills Formations, Louisville
through Brassfield Limestones,
Salamonie Dolomite, Cataract Formation
Limestone and dolomite

Ordovician

Whitewater and Dillsboro Formations,
undifferentiated rocks, and
Kope Formation
Shale and limestone

Lexington Limestone
Limestone

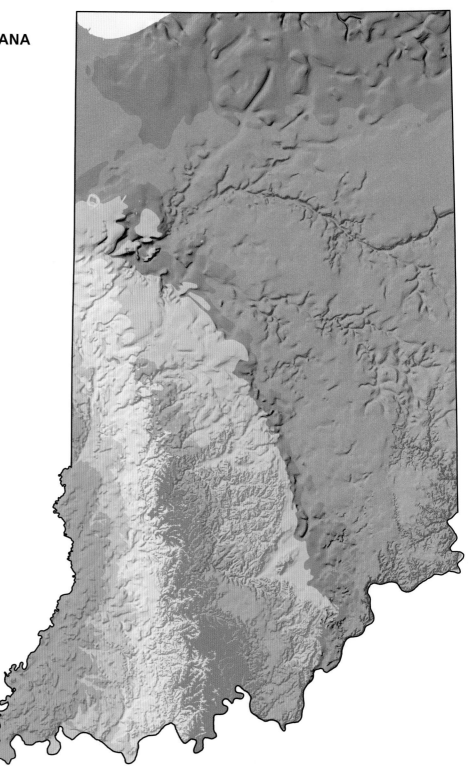

GENERALIZED STRATIGRAPHIC COLUMN OF INDIANA BEDROCK

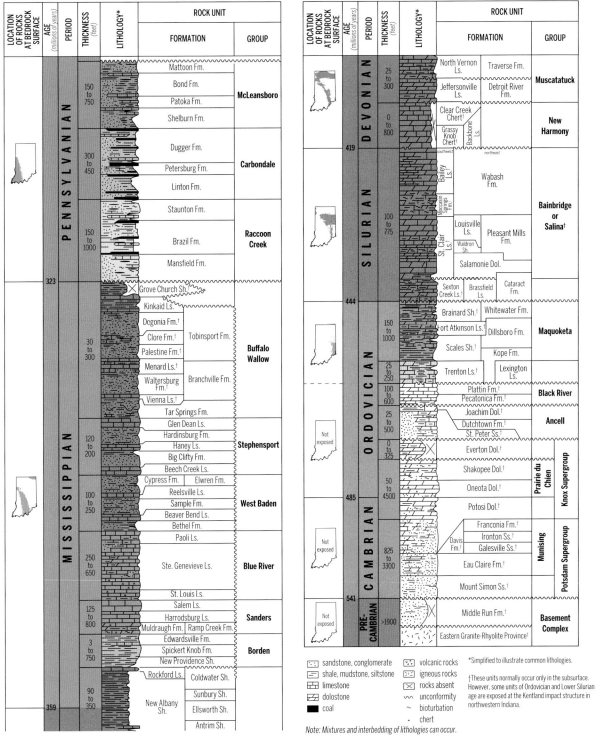

LOCATION OF ROCKS AT BEDROCK SURFACE	AGE (millions of years)	PERIOD	THICKNESS (feet)	LITHOLOGY*	ROCK UNIT FORMATION	ROCK UNIT GROUP
		PENNSYLVANIAN	150 to 750		Mattoon Fm.	McLeansboro
					Bond Fm.	
					Patoka Fm.	
					Shelburn Fm.	
			300 to 450		Dugger Fm.	Carbondale
					Petersburg Fm.	
					Linton Fm.	
			150 to 1000		Staunton Fm.	Raccoon Creek
					Brazil Fm.	
					Mansfield Fm.	
	323			✕ Grove Church Sh.		
		MISSISSIPPIAN	30 to 300		Kinkaid Ls.	
					Dogonia Fm.† / Clore Fm.† / Palestine Fm.† / Menard Ls.† / Waltersburg Fm.† / Vienna Ls.†	Tobinsport Fm. / Branchville Fm.	Buffalo Wallow
					Tar Springs Fm.	
			120 to 200		Glen Dean Ls.	Stephensport
					Hardinsburg Fm.	
					Haney Ls.	
					Big Clifty Fm.	
					Beech Creek Ls.	
			100 to 250		Cypress Fm. / Elwren Fm.	West Baden
					Reelsville Ls.	
					Sample Fm.	
					Beaver Bend Ls.	
					Bethel Fm.	
			250 to 650		Paoli Ls.	Blue River
					Ste. Genevieve Ls.	
					St. Louis Ls.	
			125 to 800		Salem Ls.	Sanders
					Harrodsburg Ls.	
					Muldraugh Fm. / Ramp Creek Fm.	
			3 to 750		Edwardsville Fm.	Borden
					Spickert Knob Fm.	
					New Providence Sh.	
			90 to 350		Rockford Ls.	Coldwater Sh.	
					New Albany Sh.	Sunbury Sh. / Ellsworth Sh. / Antrim Sh.
	359					

continued to the right

LOCATION OF ROCKS AT BEDROCK SURFACE	AGE (millions of years)	PERIOD	THICKNESS (feet)	LITHOLOGY*	ROCK UNIT FORMATION	ROCK UNIT GROUP
		DEVONIAN	25 to 300		North Vernon Ls. / Traverse Fm.	Muscatatuck
					Jeffersonville Ls. / Detroit River Fm.	
			0 to 800		Clear Creek Chert† / Grassy Knob Chert† / Backbone Ls.†	New Harmony
	419			southwest / northeast		
		SILURIAN	100 to 775		Bailey Ls.† / Wabash Fm.	Bainbridge or Salina†
					Moccasin Springs Fm.	
					Louisville Ls. / Pleasant Mills Fm.	
					St. Clair Ls.† / Waldron Sh.	
					Salamonie Dol.	
	444				Sexton Creek Ls.† / Brassfield Ls. / Cataract Fm.	
		ORDOVICIAN	150 to 1000		Brainard Sh.† / Whitewater Fm.	Maquoketa
					Fort Atkinson Ls.† / Dillsboro Fm.	
					Scales Sh.† / Kope Fm.	
			25 to 250		Trenton Ls.† / Lexington Ls.	
			100 to 600		Plattin Fm.† / Pecatonica Fm.†	Black River
			25 to 500		Joachim Dol.† / Dutchtown Fm.† / St. Peter Ss.†	Ancell
			0 to 325		✕ Everton Dol.†	
					Shakopee Dol.†	Prairie du Chien / Knox Supergroup
			50 to 4500		Oneota Dol.†	
	485				Potosi Dol.†	
		CAMBRIAN	825 to 3300		Franconia Fm.† / Davis Fm.† (Ironton Ss.† / Galesville Ss.†)	Munising / Potsdam Supergroup
					Eau Claire Fm.†	
					Mount Simon Ss.†	
	541	PRE-CAMBRIAN	>1900		✕ Middle Run Fm.†	Basement Complex
					Eastern Granite-Rhyolite Province†	

Not exposed

Legend

- sandstone, conglomerate
- shale, mudstone, siltstone
- limestone
- dolostone
- coal
- volcanic rocks
- igneous rocks
- ✕ rocks absent
- ~ unconformity
- bioturbation
- chert

*Simplified to illustrate common lithologies.

†These units normally occur only in the subsurface. However, some units of Ordovician and Lower Silurian age are exposed at the Kentland impact structure in northwestern Indiana.

Note: Mixtures and interbedding of lithologies can occur.

next 100 million years, similar rocks, although less clayey and more dolomitic and siliceous, occur. Tectonic forces from the Appalachians brought about gentle upward movement on the Cincinnati Arch, which combined with global sea-level changes to produce times when some of the rocks were exposed at the surface and were eroded by wind and water. An erosional surface, called an unconformity, exists within the sequence where rocks are missing over the arch. Of particular importance was the development of reefs during the Silurian Period that, for a portion of time, rimmed the Illinois and Michigan Basins and later, during the Devonian Period, became areas of shallow-water carbonate shoals. In the Late Devonian and Early Mississippian Periods, a deepening of sea level across the continent produced a 90-to-350-foot-thick organic-rich black shale that is traceable throughout the midcontinent. This shale is overlain by an equally impressive 700-foot-thick sequence of sandstone, siltstone, and shale deposited into deltas along the eastern margin of the Illinois Basin. This wedge of clastic sediments spread into the midcontinent from the eroding Appalachians.

As deltaic sedimentation waned, carbonate rocks accumulated during the Middle Mississippian Period. Fossiliferous limestone composed of a variety of invertebrate fossils was dominant at this time, and oolitic limestone also formed with fossiliferous limestone, the products of carbonate shoal development in warm, shallow carbonate-rich seas. The Mississippian Period is known as the Age of Crinoids, and echinoderms were a significant component of fossiliferous limestone, along with bryozoans and brachiopods. An important Middle Mississippian unit is the Salem Limestone, known by the trade name "Indiana limestone." Quarried as dimension stone, this rock is estimated to clad 50 to 75 percent of all limestone buildings in the country and graces many of the nation's most iconic structures. The Late Mississippian is represented by mixed clastic and carbonate deposition, in part from sediments derived from mountainous areas to the east but mainly from upland areas in the upper Midwest and Canada. Repeated cycles of sandstone, shale, and limestone formed during the Late Mississippian.

The end of the Mississippian Period produced a dramatic change in the Indiana landscape. A drop in sea level exposed the former sea bottom to erosion across the state, and deep valleys were carved into the Mississippian surface by roaring rivers. This extensive erosion produced an unconformity that highlights the removal of most of the Mississippian rocks in northwestern Indiana and to a lesser extent to the south. Subsequent backfilling by sand and finer-grained sediments of these primarily northeast-to-southwest-oriented valleys occurred during the Pennsylvanian Period. After the paleo-valleys were filled, vast tree-and-fern-covered swamps formed on and between deltas now building out into the reflooded Illinois Basin. Sandstone, shale, claystone, and coal were created from these sediments. Fluctuations in sea level and the amount of sediment being dumped into the basin during the Pennsylvanian Period produced numerous coal beds and an occasional fossiliferous limestone. By the end of the Pennsylvanian, Indiana once again was above sea level, beginning nearly 300 million years of continual erosion of the landscape.

It is disappointing that Indiana does not have rocks associated with the end of the Paleozoic Era, the entire Mesozoic Era, and most of the Cenozoic Era. From elsewhere we are aware of the geological history of the continent as North America separated from Europe, Africa, and South America to continue a west-northwest drift to where we are today. We are equally aware of the changes in climate, flora and fauna, and sea level over this vast time period. Dinosaurs certainly roamed across Indiana, but there are no records of them. Only in a 5-million-year-old Pliocene sinkhole in north-central Indiana have plants and animals, such as rhinoceroses, camels, bears, wolves, frogs, snakes, turtles, and several rodents, been discovered from these "missing" time periods.

The lack of a geologic record changed during the Pleistocene Epoch, starting 2.6 million years ago, when the Earth began to cool and continental-scale glaciers formed. More than a dozen cool and warm cycles alternated during the Pleistocene, and it is possible that many glaciers extended into Indiana during cool periods, but glacial records are inherently incomplete. The first recorded ice sheet to enter Indiana did

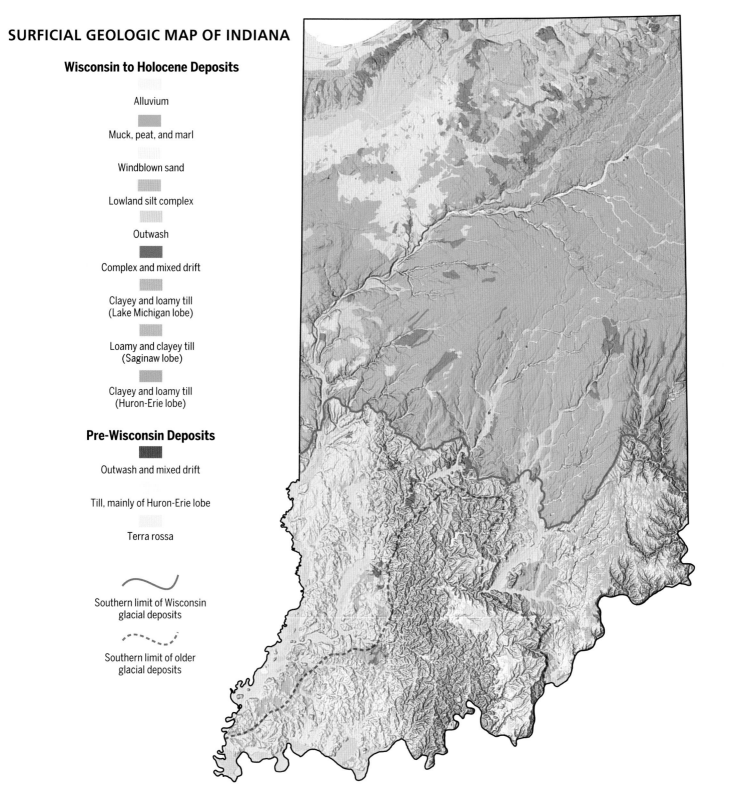

SURFICIAL GEOLOGIC MAP OF INDIANA

Wisconsin to Holocene Deposits

Alluvium

Muck, peat, and marl

Windblown sand

Lowland silt complex

Outwash

Complex and mixed drift

Clayey and loamy till
(Lake Michigan lobe)

Loamy and clayey till
(Saginaw lobe)

Clayey and loamy till
(Huron-Erie lobe)

Pre-Wisconsin Deposits

Outwash and mixed drift

Till, mainly of Huron-Erie lobe

Terra rossa

Southern limit of Wisconsin
glacial deposits

Southern limit of older
glacial deposits

so about 700,000 years ago, bringing fragments of coal, sandstone, and claystone from Michigan. This ice advanced southward, rearranging the landscape by filling valleys and diverting streams. It appears to have reached central Indiana before retreating northward. Another advance 300,000 to 132,000 years ago followed during the Illinoian Stage of glaciation. The Illinoian Stage ice extended much farther south, wrapping around an upland area in south-central Indiana, and possibly even reaching northern Kentucky. The subsequent retreat of the ice exposed the landscape for about 125,000 years, producing a recognizable soil horizon between the Illinoian Stage deposits and the younger overlying sediments.

The ice returned again about 50,000 years ago as three lobes extended out of the Lake Michigan Basin, Lake Erie Basin, and Saginaw area of Michigan. Known as the Wisconsin Stage of glaciation, ice terminated its advance south of Indianapolis 25,000 years ago, extending essentially east to west across the state. Smaller advances and retreats of Wisconsin ice produced the distinctive ridges, or moraines, in the northern half of Indiana. Deposits of gravel, sand, and clay, as well as mixed sediments called till, are directly attributable to the glaciers. The sediments are as much as 500 feet thick in northeastern Indiana and thin to only a few feet at the southern limit of the Wisconsin Stage ice.

Most of the landscapes north of the Wisconsin Stage glacial boundary are glacial in origin. The large amount of water that exited directly from the ice front flowed across the unglaciated region to the south and along major drainageways, also shaping the landscape. Sand and gravel occur in some places at the Wisconsin Stage limit, and most major drainages carried coarse-grained sediment southward. This coarse sediment frequently choked existing streams, causing them to fill up above their tributaries. Many of these tributaries were dammed and accumulated clay and silt along their valleys. Only through later downcutting of the major drainages were the tributaries able to reestablish the flow seen today.

Northwestern Indiana was also influenced by ice, but mostly by its melting. As the ice pulled back from the last moraines along the southern rim of Lake Michigan, water ponded between the moraines and the retreating ice front. Shorelines formed along the moraines, consisting of beach and dune sand with intervening wetlands filled with peats and other organic sediments. Eventually, ice retreated from the Great Lakes never to return. A complex history of lake-level change associated with rebound of the ground surface in response to the removal of the weight of ice created the last major shoreline along Lake Michigan's shore. During this shoreline's 6,000-year history, winds along and off the lake have produced some of the largest sand dunes in the world—the Indiana Dunes.

Indiana has a diverse physiography, some of which remains from millions of years ago and some of which is only tens of thousands of years old. Other areas along our lakes and rivers are molding themselves today, responding to the same Earth processes established 4.5 billion years ago.

—TODD A. THOMPSON, State Geologist of Indiana and
Director of the Indiana Geological and Water Survey

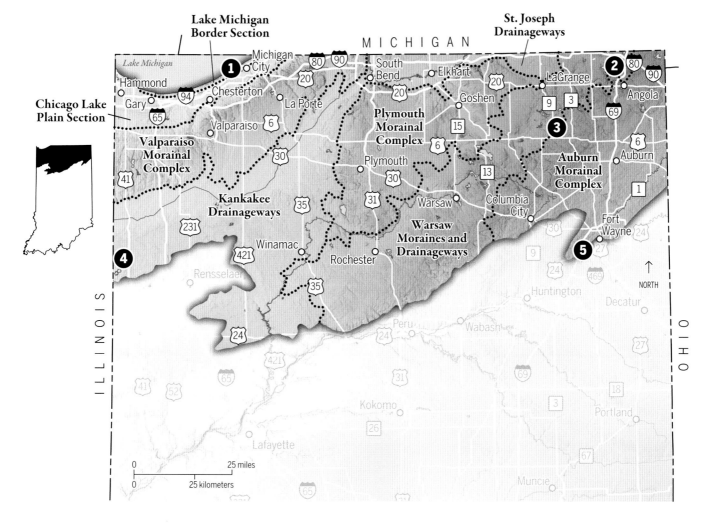

NORTHERN MORAINE AND LAKE REGION

Extinctions, widespread glaciation, and catastrophic floods have the power to shape and alter the landscape on a grand scale. In Indiana, no event has more greatly affected the topography and natural resources than the advance and retreat of continental-scale ice sheets in the past 2.6 million years, and the lasting effects are most evident in the Northern Moraine and Lake Region. Characterized by natural lakes, sand dunes, and moraine ridges, the topography of this region was created almost entirely by depositional and erosional action during the Pleistocene ice age. From the large tracts of outwash in the central drainageways to the beach ridges along the Lake Michigan Border Section, these deposits compose some of the most recently formed landforms in the state. Almost all of the state's natural lakes are in the northern region, many of which occupy kettle holes. These depressions lie between curving ridges of sand and gravel where streams once flowed beneath mile-thick lobes of ice. Overlapping ridges and irregular hills are the result of competing lobes of ice, which intermingled to form a complex network of unconsolidated sediments that cover the bedrock up to 450 feet thick.

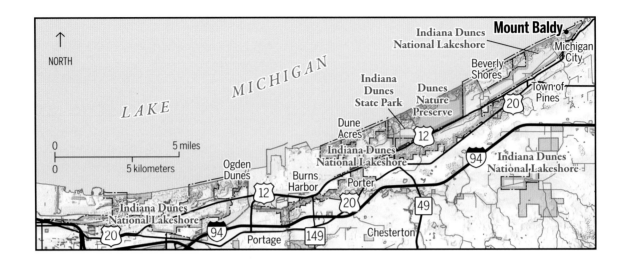

1 INDIANA DUNES
The Rise and Fall of Lake Michigan
41.6335, -87.0544

Lake Michigan—one of five Great Lakes along America's "third coast"—has experienced many changes in its relatively short lifetime (geologically speaking, of course). At the southern tip of this glacially carved basin lies a string of sandy beaches and wooded ridges known collectively as the Indiana Dunes. Formed from the redistribution of sediment after the retreat of the last ice sheet, these scenic landforms are located in Lake, Porter, and LaPorte Counties within Indiana Dunes State Park and National Lakeshore.

Toward the end of the Wisconsin Stage of glaciation, ice slowly withdrew from Indiana. Curved ridges of glacial sediment accumulated along the southern edge of the Lake Michigan lobe to form the Valparaiso Moraine and other smaller moraines. As the ice continued to retreat northward, meltwater pooled between the moraines and the ice margin, creating the earliest version of Lake Michigan around 18,000 years ago. The ice lobe fluctuated many times between 17,000 to 13,500 years ago, causing lake levels to rise and fall. These

variations produced several shorelines in the Chicagoland area, and today only two—the Glenwood Beach and the Calumet Beach—are preserved. The older Glenwood Beach remains are heavily eroded, but the younger Calumet Beach is a prominent ridge that extends alongside US 12 from Dune Acres to Michigan City.

When glacial ice retreated from the region 12,000 years ago, Lake Michigan experienced a 2,000-year-long low period. Water fell more than 100 feet below modern-day levels. Prehistoric people standing on the modern shoreline would have viewed miles of dry lakebed. However, the Earth's crust began to rise, or recoil, after the immense weight of glacial ice was removed, a phenomenon known as isostatic rebound. By around 6,000 years ago, the lake level was higher than today, and water currents began to erode sediments from the edges of the basin and deposit them along the southern rim. A barrier beach developed, forming our current shoreline— the Tolleston Beach. Lake level continued to rise, and storms

8

Foredunes are long ridges that form parallel to the shoreline, while bowl-shaped blowout dunes extend landward owing to erosion of the foredune.

washed over the beach, depositing new sand, which caused the ridge to migrate landward and grow. At 4,500 years ago, a sudden drop in lake level exposed the Tolleston Beach for the next 500 years, and sand was swept into U-shaped dunes and long foredune ridges. During the past 3,500 years, shifting winds have reworked these dunes, shaping the landscape into what we see today.

Although born from wind and water currents thousands of years ago, the dynamic ecosystems in the Indiana Dunes continue to evolve, sometimes at a daily rate. Vegetation has

Cowles Bog in Indiana Dunes National Lakeshore is one of several wetland areas formed by the vegetation of the shallow lagoon that developed during the fall from peak lake level 4,500 years ago.

The fast-growing rhizomes of dune grasses help to stabilize the sand and protect against erosion.

stabilized the sand, and wetlands and forests have developed among the dunes. Today, wind still sweeps sand from Michigan and Wisconsin onshore, and foredunes continue to form parallel to the shoreline. In areas where vegetation cover is disturbed, wind blows the sand into steep mountains called blowout dunes. To see these active forces at work, visit the Indiana Dunes Visitors Center on IN 49. Challenge yourself with climbs up Mount Baldy and Mount Tom, explore tree "graveyards" within blowout dunes where the shifting pile of sand has suffocated parts of the forest, relax on the modern Lake Michigan shoreline, or hike through Cowles Bog for an experience unlike any other in the Hoosier State.

2 POKAGON STATE PARK
Kettles, Kames, and Moraines
41.7080, -85.0092

Wooded mounds protrude between swampy bogs and clear lakes at Pokagon State Park, located 5 miles northwest of Angola in Steuben County. The park's uneven terrain is part of a morainal landscape that formed approximately 17,000 years ago during the last phases of the Wisconsin Stage of glaciation. When massive continental glaciers began to retreat toward Canada, the melting ice released piles of unsorted rock and sediment (till) in its wake. Different from the sharply curved recessional moraines near Fort Wayne and Valparaiso that mark major pauses in glacial movement, these small, discontinuous mounds were deposited between the Saginaw and Huron-Erie lobes during their race to retreat northward.

The two ice lobes competed for ground space, each overriding and burying the other, leaving the irregular moraines seen today. This process roughened the surface of the ice, and large crevasses formed. Meltwater enlarged these fractures, carrying sediment on top of and underneath the glacier.

When the ice retreated from northeastern Indiana, meltwater streams flowed past hummocky moraines, and up to 400 feet of glacial sediment covered the bedrock surface. The piles of sand and gravel that accumulated inside glacial crevasses remain as sharp-crested hills called kames, named for the sawtooth shape of a rooster's comb. Blocks of ice that broke off the main ice lobes melted slowly over hundreds or even thousands of years, forming kettle hole depressions. Some of these holes filled with water to create lakes, such as Lake Lonidaw and Lake James. The smooth, rounded boulders and cobbles that are prevalent throughout the park are also evidence of the area's icy past. Called erratics, these specimens of granite, basalt, gneiss, and other igneous and metamorphic rocks were plucked from Canadian bedrock, smoothed by erosion, and left by glaciers.

Although humans have developed the surrounding areas, the Pokagon landscape remains relatively unchanged since the end of the last ice age. To visit, park at the Potawatomi Inn and take in the sweeping lake views before exploring one of the park's seven easy to moderate trails. Trail 5 leads to the sandy shores of Lake James before climbing an erratic-lined path up a tree-topped kame, while Trail 1 leads south along the lake through gentle wooded moraines. Trail 3 travels 2.2 miles through the Potawatomi Nature Preserve to Hell's Point, a large kame hill that rises 135 feet above Lake James. Climb the tiered staircase for a panoramic view before taking the 320-foot spur to an observation deck at the edge of Lake Lonidaw.

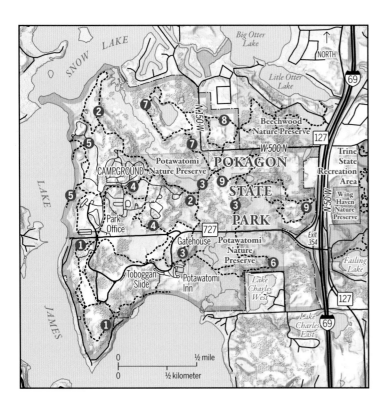

Plucked from Canadian bedrock and transported by glacial ice, erratics are evidence of the continental glaciers that covered the park several times during the Pleistocene Epoch.

Lake Lonidaw and other kettle lakes are ringed with marshes and wetlands. —Courtesy of the Indiana Department of Natural Resources

3 CHAIN O'LAKES STATE PARK
Interconnected Glacial Waterways
41.3413, -85.4021

Bead-like strings of shimmering lakes, rolling hills and ridges, and marshy peat bogs at Chain O'Lakes State Park collectively form one of the finest examples of kettle and kame topography in the Midwest. Located 5 miles southeast of Albion in Noble County, the 1-mile-wide park packs more than 200 acres of waterways into a 4-mile-long stretch that bears witness to the continental ice sheets of the Pleistocene Epoch. Nine of the park's thirteen glacial lakes are interconnected by meltwater channels, forming a chain that gives the park its name.

The series of lakes here formed approximately 17,000 years ago during the end of the Wisconsin Stage of glaciation. As the Huron-Erie lobe retreated to the northeast toward Ohio and Canada, large blocks of ice detached from the main glacier and were buried by sand and gravel. The ice melted slowly to form deep basins called kettles, and sediment on top of the ice remained as rounded hills, known as kames. Meltwater streams flowed around the kames, linking the kettles to create the interconnected lakes you see today. Some of the smaller kettle lakes have filled in with peat, an organic-rich material, and these filled depressions form the low-lying swamps and bogs located near the larger lakes.

The northeast and southwest corners of the park are home to the Glacier Esker Nature Preserve, named for a long, winding ridge that rises high above the kettle lakes. As fractures developed within the Huron-Erie lobe, meltwater streams carried sand and gravel beneath the ice. After the ice melted away, these sediments remained as a narrow ridge called an

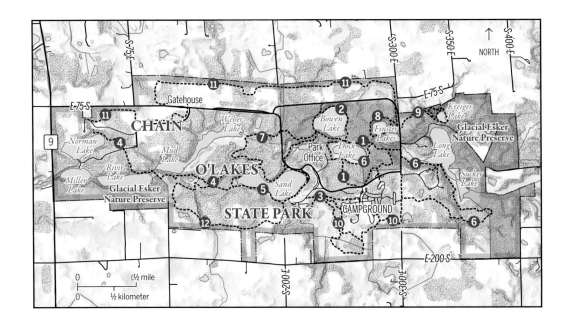

All thirteen lakes at Chain O'Lakes State Park (including Little Finster Lake shown here) are known as kettle lakes and formed from the melting of buried blocks of ice during the last ice age. —Courtesy of the Indiana Department of Natural Resources

esker. The esker at Chain O'Lakes State Park is considered the best example of this geological feature in the state.

Over 20 miles of trails traverse the rolling hills, ravines, and lakeshores at Chain O'Lakes. The best time to visit is in the spring and summer, when you can rent a canoe or kayak at the Sand Lake boat launch and explore the glacial waterways up close. Take a full day to paddle the winding channels through all nine interconnected lakes: Miller, Rivir, Mud, Weber, Sand, Bowen, Dock, Long, and Sucker Lakes. Many of the hiking trails follow moderate 1-to-2-mile loops around wooded lakeshores and connecting channels. Take Trail 8 for a moderately rugged self-guided trek that crosses the kame between Finster Lakes, and continue west on Trail 1 to the north side of Dock Lake to experience the rise and swell of the esker ridge.

The low-lying wetlands and bogs around Bowen, Kreiger, and Sucker Lakes are former kettles that have partially filled in with sediment. —Courtesy of the Indiana Department of Natural Resources

KANKAKEE SANDS PRESERVE
Glacial Floodway Turned Prairie Dunes
41.0468, -87.4494

The wooded dunes and expansive grasslands at Kankakee Sands Preserve are an unusual geological destination in the Hoosier State that you won't want to miss. Located about 7 miles north of Morocco in Newton County, this gently rolling landscape was once the scene of a catastrophic meltwater flood that birthed one of the largest wetlands in North America. Although unassuming at first glance, Kankakee Sands is one of the most significant legacies of the Pleistocene Epoch in northwestern Indiana.

Kankakee Sands is a tallgrass sand prairie established on scattered dunes that overlie thick gravel and interbedded sand. Unique to the American Midwest, tallgrass prairie ecosystems are adapted to the rich soils that develop in glaciated regions. The low-lying plain here began to form 21,000 years ago, when the Lake Michigan and Saginaw lobes started to retreat from Indiana near the end of the Wisconsin Stage of glaciation. Sediment-laden meltwater poured off the melting ice and pooled in large lakes north of a moraine. Lake levels rose higher and higher, and the moraine began to weaken. Around 19,000 years ago, a catastrophic flood erupted in an event known as the Kankakee Torrent. Fast-moving floodwaters raced down the Kankakee River, ripping up the underlying Silurian-age bedrock to form deep gorges and rubble terraces in a matter of days. When the floodwaters receded, a vast outwash plain of sand and gravel spread along the river's edge to form the Grand Kankakee Marsh.

Covering nearly 1 million acres across northern Indiana and Illinois, the Grand Kankakee Marsh was once one of the largest wetlands in North America. Westerly winds reworked the outwash plain's sandy surface into small dunes and flats between 14,000 and 12,000 years ago. Large herds of bison and flocks of waterfowl gathered near the shallow waters. Rivaling the Everglades for biodiversity, the marsh was called "Chicago's food pantry" in the 1800s for the abundant game that it yielded. Change came after the Civil War, however, when settlers began to drain the marsh to use the fertile soil for agriculture. By the 1930s, the Kankakee River had been dredged into a 90-mile ditch and 99 percent of the Grand Kankakee Marsh had been destroyed.

Recent conservation efforts by The Nature Conservancy helped to restore and protect 7,800 acres of this shrinking sand prairie ecosystem. To visit, park at the Kankakee Sands office on US 41 and head north to the Wet Prairie (Unit K) Trail. An easy 0.6-mile loop leads through water-loving sedges and grasslands on the edges of a bison field. To the north, you can follow the Conrad Station Savanna Trail through rolling sand dunes and an ephemeral wetland on a moderate 1.5-mile loop or trek to the top of a sand dune along the 2-mile Grace Teninga Discovery Trail. Visit in the summer to see the vibrant yellow blooms of prickly pear cactus and other native flowers, or watch migratory birds in the fall.

Herds of bison roam the restored tallgrass prairie.
—Courtesy of Steven Higgs, Natural Bloomington

The seasonal wetlands at Kankakee Sands are a geologic landscape left over from a massive flood that occurred 19,000 years ago near the end of the Wisconsin Stage of glaciation.

17

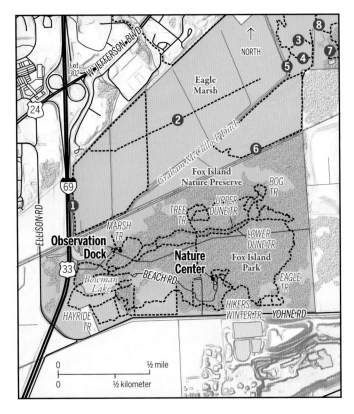

5 FOX ISLAND COUNTY PARK
Wooded Dunes along a Glacial Sluiceway
41.0163, -85.2388

In the late 1600s, French explorers journeyed along the headwaters of the Wabash River and found a series of small wooded dune "islands" elevated above a vast marshy expanse. Reworked from the outwash of a catastrophic glacial flood, these dunes sparked Fort Wayne's nickname as the Summit City and today form the scenic ridges at Fox Island County Park. Located 9 miles from downtown Fort Wayne in Allen County, the 605-acre natural area features 6 miles of trails along sand dune ridges, seasonal ponds, and wetlands.

Approximately 18,000 years ago, the Huron-Erie lobe was located near Fort Wayne during the glacier's slow retreat northeast toward Ohio and Canada. Each time the massive ice front readvanced, broad ridges of till, called moraines, were deposited along the outer margin of the glacier. One of the largest is the Fort Wayne Moraine, a widely arcing ridge that extends from southern Michigan through Fort Wayne into northwestern Ohio. As the glacier continued to melt, water pooled between the shrinking ice front and the Fort Wayne Moraine to form Glacial Lake Maumee. Similar in size to modern Lake Erie, this ancient lake blanketed Allen County with thick sediment, and small beach ridges and spits marked the margins of the lake. Around 17,000 years ago, the lake burst through a low point in the moraine, releasing a catastrophic rush of water known as the Maumee Torrent. The flood gouged a 1-mile-wide, 30-mile-long scar into the landscape, a feature called the Wabash-Erie Channel.

Glacial Lake Maumee continued to drain southwest to the Wabash River through the Wabash-Erie Channel for about 1,000 years. Wetlands developed along the channel margin, and westerly winds reworked sand from the outwash terraces into small inland dunes. When the continental glaciers had finally shrunk back into Canada, Glacial Lake Maumee drained and the flow of water down the channel became negligible. Today, the Little River, a small channelized stream that flows just south of Fox Island County Park along Yohne Road, follows the course of the Wabash-Erie Channel and remains a vestige of the river network established after the Maumee Torrent.

Although the wetlands are a visible link to the ancient glacial sluiceway that once existed here, the most striking topographic feature at Fox Island is its dunes. Low patches of sand are visible near the parking lot to the east of Bowman Lake. To the north, larger wooded dunes rise 20 to 30 feet above the valley and extend about 1,000 feet along the southern edge of the nature preserve. The Upper Dune Trail straddles the peak of a 30-foot-high dune, while the Lower Dune Trail follows along the base. Hike to the observation dock for a view of the open ponds, wetlands, and sandy ridges. The Nature Center has an excellent overview of the regional geology, and the Geo Garden displays some large glacial erratics north of the main entrance.

The wooded dunes include exposures of sand made of quartz, garnet, magnetite, and other minerals that were scoured from Canadian bedrock and deposited by glacial ice.

Seasonal marshes at Fox Island County Park are remnants of the Wabash-Erie Channel, a path forged by an ice age flood known as the Maumee Torrent.

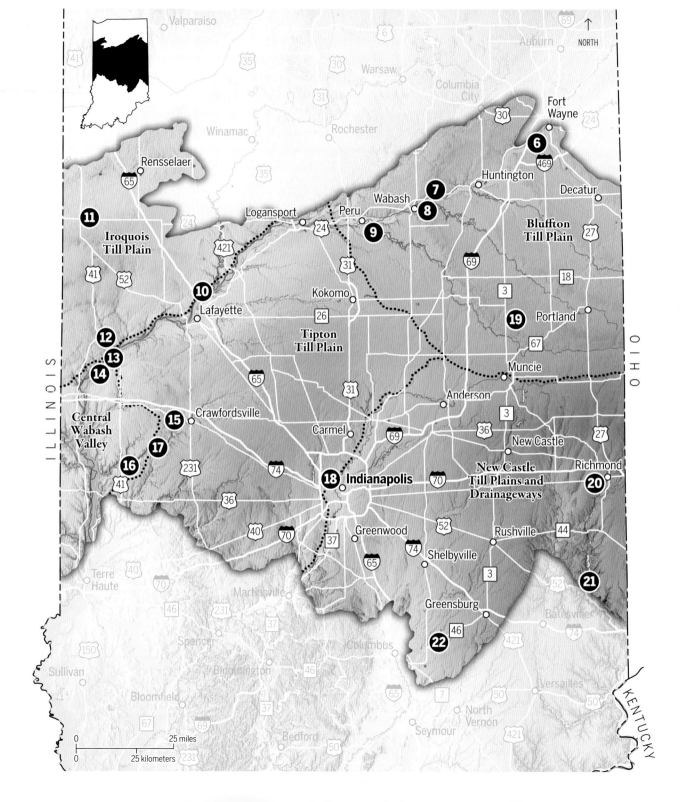

CENTRAL TILL PLAIN REGION

Positioned between kettle lakes and moraines to the north and bedrock hills and valleys to the south, the Central Till Plain tells the story of Indiana's transition from tropical sea to ice-covered tundra. Bound by the southern limit of the Wisconsin Stage of glaciation, the region is characterized by thick deposits of unconsolidated clay, sand, and gravel that form broad, sweeping plains. As large sheets of ice advanced and retreated over this area many times from 2.6 million to 10,000 years ago, the underlying bedrock was scoured and covered by hundreds of feet of outwash, till, and lake sediments. Concentric ridges in the Bluffton Till Plain mark the progressive advance and retreat of ice from the Huron-Erie lobe, and major drainageways flow along the outer edges of these moraines. Sand and gravel carried and deposited by water that poured off the melting glacier now form well-drained farmlands with rich, even-textured soil in the Tipton Till Plain. Within the Central Wabash Valley and New Castle Till Plains, glacial meltwater carved deeply entrenched valleys to expose Paleozoic-age strata in rugged cliffs and gorges below the low-relief plains. Today, the complex network of unconsolidated deposits that covers Indiana's midsection forms the backbone of the state's aggregate resources and groundwater repositories.

6 ARDMORE QUARRY
Carbonate Rock Crushed for Aggregate
41.0287, -85.1970

From the roads you drive to the water you drink, our modern lives depend on a wealth of natural resources that come from the Earth. About 5 miles southwest of downtown Fort Wayne in Allen County, the Ardmore Quarry annually produces 3 million tons of one of these valuable resources—crushed stone called aggregate—from horizontal layers of Silurian and Devonian strata. In operation since the 1950s, this aggregate quarry offers a unique opportunity to view the extraction of critical earth materials within the Bluffton Till Plain.

Known locally as "the gravel pit," the Ardmore Quarry is one of several quarries that produces crushed stone from Silurian and Devonian rock in the Fort Wayne area. These fine-grained, occasionally fossiliferous units of limestone and dolostone are the remnants of fossil reefs that thrived here approximately 400 million years ago. The oldest formation exposed is the Louisville Limestone, a gray dolomitic limestone that bulges out

along the base of the quarry walls. Above it lies about 96 feet of soft, light-gray, shaly dolostone and well-bedded fossiliferous limestone from the Wabash Formation. Above the thick Silurian-age units, about 40 feet of thin, brownish limestone, dolostone, and shale from the Detroit River and Traverse Formations are visible at the top of the quarry. These two Devonian-age

The observation tower at Ardmore Quarry is one of the few places in the state where you can view aggregate being mined.

units, as well as the unconsolidated sediments that overlie them, are considered waste. This overburden, as it is known, is gathered into large piles along the edges of the quarry pit and sold as flagstone pavers and construction fill. As the quarry continues to mine to greater depths, the pit expands laterally and new overburden is removed before extracting the carbonate rock below.

At Ardmore, carbonate rock is blasted from the quarry walls three to four times a week. Wheel loaders move the extracted rock to large crushers, which break apart and sort the rock into coarse- and fine-grained sizes. These aggregates are used in building and construction. Sand, gravel, and crushed stone are the primary natural aggregates produced in Indiana, and many everyday products are made from them—including concrete, asphalt, glass, steel, household cleaners, makeup, medicine, paint, fertilizer, wallboard, agricultural lime, animal feed, and food additives. To visit, head south on Ardmore Avenue and turn west by the old Elmhurst High School onto Sand Point Road, following it a half mile to the quarry entrance on the left. Climb the stairs to the observation deck and peer down into the 200-foot-deep pit for a superb view of the active aggregate operations.

Quarry operators feed blasted pieces of limestone and dolostone into jaw crushers, where they are broken into various sizes and transported on conveyors.

Horizontal layers of Devonian- and Silurian-age carbonate rock along the eastern wall of the Ardmore Quarry.

HANGING ROCK NATURE PRESERVE

7

Pinnacle Reefs Form Klintar Cliffs

40.8297, -85.7084

Many teardrop-shaped ridges are scattered along the Upper Wabash Valley. Called "klintar" for the Scandinavian term for "rocky," these protruding abutments in the Bluffton Till Plain are the remnants of ancient fossil reefs that thrived here more than 420 million years ago. The peculiar structures are concen-trated in the 15-mile stretch of gently rolling agricultural land between Andrews and Wabash. The most prominent klint is Hanging Rock, located in a nature preserve along the Wabash River 1.5 miles southeast of Lagro.

During the Silurian Period, warm, oxygenated seas flooded the early North American continent to form an inland sea. Corals, stromatoporoids, and other mound-building organisms thrived in the shallow waters and formed belts of tall, cylindrical reefs (pinnacles) along the margins of the Illinois and Michigan Basins. Buried by subsequent deposition and glacial sediments, these reefs remained hidden until a surge of glacial floodwater known as the Maumee Torrent scoured the landscape 17,000 years ago. More resistant than the surrounding strata, the reef structures stood their ground against the fast-moving waters.

Hanging Rock, a remnant of one such Silurian-age pinnacle reef, towers 84 feet above the Wabash River. The rocky monolith is composed of three rock layers within the Wabash Formation. Soft, gray, shaly dolostone of the Mississinewa Shale

Hanging Rock is a classic example of a Silurian reef structure. These features are known as klintar (singular: klint) and form protruding mounds and bluffs along the Wabash River.

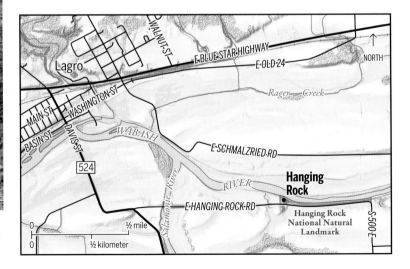

Dedicated as a National Natural Landmark, Hanging Rock rises more than 80 feet high to overlook the Wabash River.

Member is exposed along the riverbank, and above it lies two layers from the Liston Creek Limestone. Well-bedded, tan limestone and dolostone form the majority of the reef structure, and a hard, massive dark gray dolostone layer caps the top. Few fossils are recognizable in the reef structure because dolomitization, the process of calcite being converted to dolomite, obscures the identifying features of the fossils.

The Hanging Rock you see today is only a small portion of the original reef that once extended across the present-day Wabash River. The erosive power of the Maumee Torrent, followed by continued weathering of the river, have worn away the northern flank and central core of the reef, leaving only a hanging ledge that gives the structure its name. To visit, take IN 524 south of Lagro and keep left to stay on East Hanging Rock Road. Park on the north side of the road and follow the moderate, well-worn path to the riverbank. The 0.3-mile trail circles around the ancient reef and offers unparalleled views of the Upper Wabash Valley from the top.

BIG FOUR RAILROAD CUT
8 The Wabash Reef in Cross Section
40.7969, -85.8146

The Upper Wabash Valley in northern Indiana contains some of the finest exposures of Silurian fossil reefs in North America. Formed by ancient reef-building organisms, these crag-like bastions of resistant dolostone were scoured by floodwater at the end of the Pleistocene Epoch. One of the best-known exposures is the Wabash Reef, located along the Big Four Railroad Cut in downtown Wabash. This feature inspired generations of geologists and informed much of what is known about Silurian reefs in the Upper Midwest.

Approximately 420 million years ago, North America was covered by a vast inland sea. Separated by deeper basins to the northeast and southwest, a carbonate platform extended across portions of Indiana and patches of reefs flourished in the shallow waters. Over time these carbonate deposits became the Wabash Formation. Widespread glaciation in the Pleistocene Epoch buried the Silurian-age strata under thick deposits of glacial drift. As the ice retreated, water from Glacial Lake Maumee flooded the Upper Wabash Valley and swept away loose sediment and soft bedrock, leaving the massive dolomite reef structures to protrude from the river valley.

Unlike Hanging Rock and other Silurian-age reefs that were exhumed by torrents of floodwater, the Wabash Reef was excavated by the Big Four Railroad in 1896. Stretching 750 feet in length, this enduring exposure rises 40 feet above the tracks to render an impressive cross section of a domed reef structure. The massive reef core is made of exceptionally pure fine-grained dolostone and measures about 250 feet across. Thin inclined beds of the Mississinewa Shale Member of the Wabash Formation drape along the flanks of the reef core, and shale layers interfinger with thick wedges of

dolomite along its edges. Although called a reef, it is closer in composition to a deep sea mud mound, and few fossils are recognizable owing to the process of dolomite mineral replacement. The top of the reef is nearly flat as a result of erosion, and the bottom of the reef is up to 65 feet below the level of the tracks.

To visit the Big Four Railroad Cut in Wabash, park in the small lot at Paradise Spring Historical Park and walk northeast to where the paved path crosses the railroad tracks. The exposure is located on private railroad property and can be safely observed only from the city park. Be aware that the rail line is active, so view this impressive structure from afar.

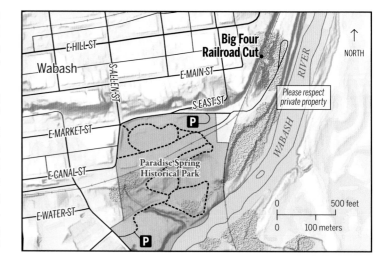

The Wabash Reef was uncovered when the Big Four (Cleveland, Cincinnati, Chicago, and St. Louis) Railroad excavated the section in 1896.

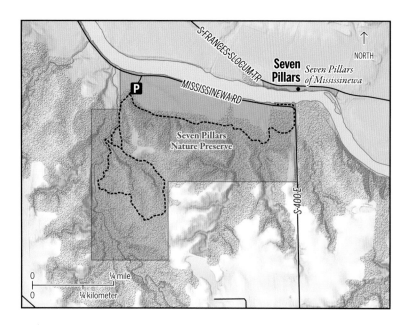

SEVEN PILLARS OF THE MISSISSINEWA
Alcoves in Cherty Limestone
40.7254, -85.9951

Along the north bank of the Mississinewa River in Miami County, about 5 miles southeast of Peru, are seven curious limestone pillars standing about 25 to 50 feet above low water. The Seven Pillars of the Mississinewa were created by the erosive power of water on Silurian limestone. These rounded buttresses and rocky nooks are a little-known natural feature in the morainal landscape of north-central Indiana and have long been used as a communal gathering place by the Miami Nation of Indians.

The Mississinewa River flows 100 miles northwest through the Bluffton Till Plain before joining the Wabash River near Peru. The river's swift, rushing waters often make the sound suggested by the name Mis-sis-sin-e-wa, which means "falling waters" in the language of the Miamis. The rapid flow carved many features into the region's low flat valleys, but the most notable is Seven Pillars. The rounded columns are composed of the Liston Creek Limestone Member of the Wabash Formation, a cherty limestone with thin slabby beds. Over centuries, water weathered away the thinly bedded limestone along a well-developed joint pattern to produce the seven pillars. The scouring action of the river continues to smooth these structures into hourglass-shaped columns with recessed grotto-like alcoves. Although similar in shape to Jug Rock (see site 38), the Seven Pillars are still attached to the limestone bluff of the river and thus are not true freestanding rocks.

An unmaintained footpath known locally as the Frances Slocum Trail traverses the tops of the bluffs, but the best view of this scenic landform is from the opposite side of the stream. To visit, park at the Seven Pillars Nature Preserve on Mississinewa Road and follow the moderate 0.5-mile-long trail through the woods to the viewing area on the southern bank of the river.

The nature preserve is named for the seven limestone pillars that stretch along the northern bank of the Mississinewa River.

The Mississinewa River cut through till deposited by the Huron-Erie lobe to form a low, flat valley with sculpted rock features.

The flat, rolling landscape of the Lafayette region overlies the valley of the ancient Teays River, which flowed from West Virginia to Illinois more than 2.6 million years ago. A mile wide and up to 500 feet deep, this massive river valley was buried by glacial debris during the Illinoian and Wisconsin Stages of glaciation. When the ice retreated, meltwater poured across the land to carve the Wabash River, and a series of terraces formed

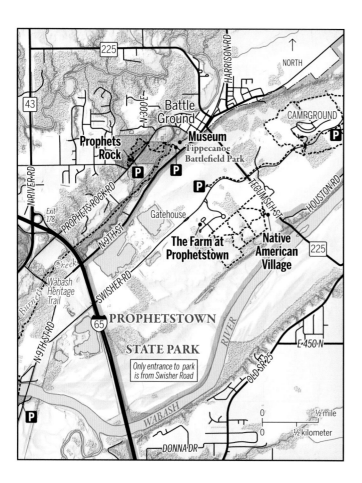

as the water levels changed. In this ice age landscape northwest of Lafayette, the small town of Battle Ground marks a bloody clash that paved the way for statehood, and its folklore underscores an interesting connection to the devastating New Madrid earthquakes in the early nineteenth century.

In 1808, Shawnee brothers Tecumseh and Tenskwatawa (the Prophet) established a new Native American settlement near the confluence of the Wabash and Tippecanoe Rivers. Called Prophet's Town, the village served as the capital of a unified Indian confederacy that opposed US expansion into the northwestern Indiana Territory. Warriors from many nations gathered at Prophet's Town, and Tecumseh angrily warned that "the very earth shall shake" those who did not join him.

White settlers grew uneasy as tensions mounted at Prophet's Town. On November 6, 1811, Governor William Henry Harrison arrived with an army and set up camp on a high terrace that overlooked a lower marshy area along the Wabash River. Fearing an attack, the Prophet ordered his men to strike before dawn on November 7. The warriors worked their way across the floodplain and up Burnett Creek to reach the encampment, but they were quickly spotted. Within two hours, the confederation retreated and the battle was over.

The bloody defeat at the Battle of Tippecanoe signaled the end of multitribal resistance, and its legacy would help William Henry Harrison later win the presidency with the campaign slogan "Tippecanoe and Tyler, Too." Almost one month after the defeat, Tecumseh's warning came to fruition and the "very earth [shook]" in the New Madrid earthquakes of 1811–1812. Centered along the Mississippi River near New Madrid, Missouri, six magnitude 6.0 to 7.5 earthquakes and more than 2,000 aftershocks trembled across the central and eastern United States in a three-month period. About 150 miles south of Lafayette, the second floor of Governor Harrison's home in Vincennes (Grouseland) cracked; farther south, in Missouri and Arkansas, the ground ruptured, sand blows shot into the air, and the Mississippi River appeared to flow backward through crashing waves. Many tribes believed that Tecumseh had predicted the quakes, and it strengthened his circle of influence. You can visit the site of Harrison's encampment at the Tippecanoe Battlefield Park and Museum, and hike the terraces and floodplains of the Wabash River at Prophetstown State Park.

A marble obelisk marks the location of the Battle of Tippecanoe.

From Delphi to Lafayette, the Wabash River overlaps the ancient Teays River Valley, and there is a noticeable widening of the river in the area of Prophetstown State Park. —Courtesy of Steven Higgs, Natural Bloomington

KENTLAND DOME
11 *Meteor Impact Structure*
40.7665, -87.3879

The Kentland Dome is one of Indiana's most enigmatic structures. Located in Newton County, this geologic anomaly has puzzled geologists for more than 130 years. Ordovician-age rocks are uplifted more than 2,000 feet above Devonian and Mississippian strata to form a structural dome among the flat-lying Quaternary-age sediments that drape the surrounding area. Best interpreted as a meteor impact feature, the highly deformed rocks present a rare look at Indiana's bedrock in the Iroquois Till Plain.

The Kentland Dome is located on the extreme northeastern margin of the Illinois Basin. Rock layers regionally dip less than 1 degree off the southwestern flank of the Kankakee Arch and are covered by up to 30 feet of till from the Wisconsin Stage of glaciation. At Kentland, however, Ordovician rocks, which typically lie more than 2,000 feet below the surface, are folded, fractured, and exposed at the surface in a nearly vertical position. Nearly 7 miles across, the complexly deformed structure is broken by faults on its southern and western flanks. The oldest rocks in the center of the dome are Ordovician-age Shakopee Dolomite, and the surrounding rock dips radially outward to the Mississippian-age Borden Group. Faults cut a stream channel filled with Pennsylvanian-age sediments on the southwestern side of the dome. The Rogers Group Inc. operates an active quarry in the center of the Kentland Dome, quarrying 500 feet of Ordovician rock for aggregate that would otherwise be inaccessible.

Many theories have been proposed to account for the unusual structures at Kentland, including a volcanic explosion, faulting, and salt dome collapse. Signs of intense stress such as angular rock fragments (breccia) and small fracture-filled dikes give some clues, but the presence of shatter cones and coesite, a silica mineral formed only under intense pressures, support the theory of origin by extraterrestrial impact. We do not know when the meteor hurtled into the Earth other than it was sometime after the end of the Pennsylvanian Period (299 million years ago), when channel sediments were faulted, but before the Pleistocene Epoch (2.6 million years ago), when ice sheets scoured the exposed bedrock units and deposited a blanket of glacial drift. To see this mysterious structure, call the Rogers Group office and schedule a time to visit the observation deck that overlooks the north and west rims of the quarry. Tours are available for school groups upon request.

Distinct funnel-shaped features known as shatter cones form when an intense burst of force occurs directly above rock.

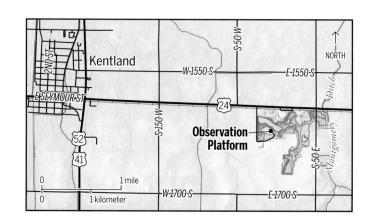

Ordovician-age carbonate strata are overlain by a very thin layer of flat-lying glacial till along a quarry wall.

Black River Group carbonates and the St. Peter Sandstone are tilted to nearly vertical positions.

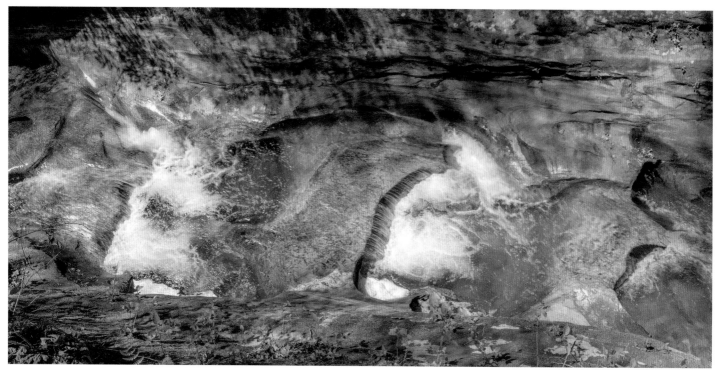

The canyon walls and floor have been smoothed by centuries of stream erosion.

12 FALL CREEK GORGE NATURE PRESERVE
Potholes in Polished Sandstone
40.3392, -87.3149

About 4 miles northwest of Williamsport in Warren County, a series of deeply carved bedrock depressions send water swirling down a narrow canyon at Fall Creek Gorge. Nicknamed the Potholes, this scenic nature preserve is known for the semicircular depressions that line the streambed. Rivulets of clear water rush over Pennsylvanian-age bedrock to form one of the most interesting areas in the Iroquois Till Plain.

After glacial ice retreated at the end of the Pleistocene Epoch, new drainage patterns collected to form Fall Creek. Meltwater quickly cut through sand, gravel, and till to expose sand-

stone from the Mansfield Formation, and the rapidly flowing waters abraded the sand, deepening the channel. Fall Creek became entrenched, or trapped, in the freshly carved gorge as it flowed east toward Big Pine Creek and the Wabash River. Smooth, bowl-shaped holes, called potholes, formed when swirling eddies of water carrying loose rocks ground into the streambed. The potholes at Fall Creek are exceptionally large for the size of the modern stream, reaching up to 5 feet in depth and 20 feet in diameter, because the stream volume was much larger during the ice age.

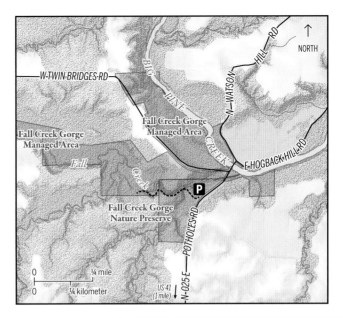

Swirling currents of water grind loose rocks into the underlying streambed to form deep circular depressions called potholes.

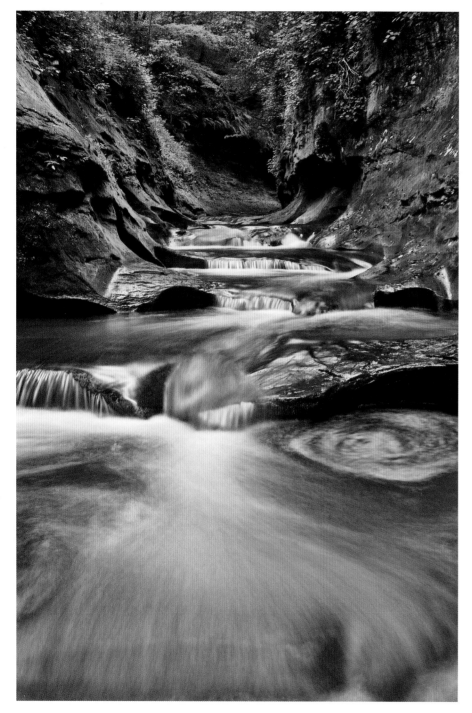

Vertical moss-covered exposures of sandstone from the Mansfield Formation loom over Fall Creek Gorge. —Courtesy of Lee Mandrell, Leman's Studios

The best time to visit Fall Creek Gorge is in the spring and fall, when abundant water flows over the streambed. Visitation is high during the summer months, and the trail can be difficult to access after heavy rains. To see the potholes, take US 41 north from Williamsport and turn north on Potholes Road (N 025 E). A small parking lot is located about 1.5 miles from US 41 but is limited to seven cars, so arrive early to secure a spot. Follow the short wooded path and climb the stairs down to the south branch of Fall Creek. When you reach exposed bedrock, carefully cross over the slotted tributary channel and look upstream to see the potholes filled with swirling water. A moderate 1.1-mile-long trail follows a flat-topped ridge on the southern rim of Fall Creek and offers scenic overlooks of the gorge and deep pothole pools below. A small waterfall, located at the western terminus of the trail, cascades over a sandstone ledge on its descent through the serene, water-polished gorge.

13 WILLIAMSPORT FALLS
Indiana's Highest Free-Falling Waterfall
40.2863, -87.2930

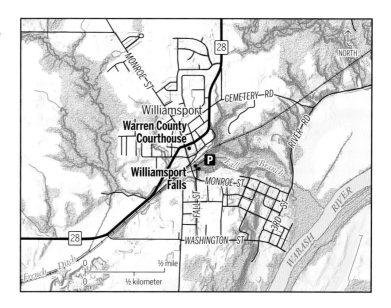

Narrow, plunging falls cascade 90 feet over a sandstone ledge at Williamsport Falls, the tallest free-falling waterfall in Indiana. Located 0.2 mile south of the Warren County Courthouse in Williamsport, water from Fall Branch tumbles over the falls before flowing southeast to the Wabash River. The waterfall's thick ledge is composed of sandstone from the Pennsylvanian-age Mansfield Formation, and the lower plunge pool is made of siltstone and shale of the Mississippian-age Borden Group. The Mansfield lies unconformably over the Borden because of an extensive erosional event that scoured bedrock around the state in the beginning of the Pennsylvanian Period.

The dramatic shape of Williamsport Falls is a testament to the abrasive action of water over time. The Pennsylvanian bedrock in this area was covered by thick sheets of glacial sediment left behind from the Illinoian and Wisconsin Stages of glaciation. As the ice retreated and stream patterns organized, water cut down through the unconsolidated deposits until it reached the resistant sandstone ridge. The stream gradually eroded away the softer rock below, undercutting the sandstone caprock until it collapsed and fell into the gorge below. The course of the creek is fixed in an eroded channel on the top of the sandstone ledge, giving the impression that water shoots out from the cliffside.

Because Fall Branch flows intermittently, the best views of Williamsport Falls are after a heavy rain or snowmelt. Park in the small lot to the north of the intersection of East Monroe and Fall Streets. From the falls, an easy 1.6-mile trail follows the creek through a wooded valley, providing good views of the waterfall base and an abandoned quarry that supplied stone for the construction of the Warren County Courthouse.

Fall Branch continues to erode the bedrock at Williamsport Falls, evidenced by large boulders of Mansfield Formation sandstone that have collapsed into the streambed below.
—Courtesy of Lee Mandrell, Leman's Studios

14 PORTLAND ARCH NATURE PRESERVE
Natural Bridge in Cross-Bedded Sandstone
40.2188, -87.3337

The massive cross-beds and towering canyon walls at Portland Arch Nature Preserve can inspire awe in even the well-traveled nature lover. Located about 7 miles southwest of Attica in Fountain County, Portland Arch is a 15-foot-wide natural archway in iron-rich sandstone of the Pennsylvanian-age Mansfield Formation. Known for its high perpendicular cliffs and scenic archway, this nature preserve is a rocky oasis in the heart of the Central Wabash Valley.

Known to be an early settlement for Native Americans, a resting place for early frontiersmen, a recreational retreat for Boy Scouts, and now a National Natural Landmark, the

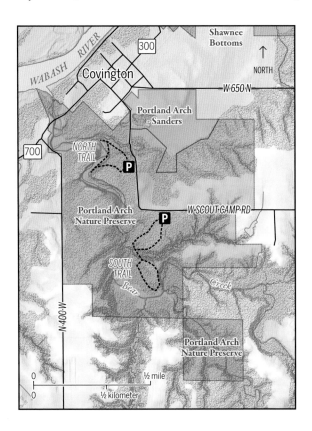

dramatic sandstone gorge at Portland Arch was chiseled by persistently flowing water. Approximately 21,000 years ago, near the end of the Pleistocene Epoch, torrents of glacial meltwater rushed through this area toward the nearby Wabash River. The fast-moving waters washed away layers of unconsolidated sediment and sculpted the underlying sandstone into narrow ridges and bluffs. Bear Creek became trapped in the bedrock gorge. A smaller tributary stream battered the sandy rock layers until, over time, it cut a hole through the ridge to form the Portland Arch.

The ridge at the archway is about 40 feet high and composed of yellow and buff-colored sandstone. Upstream, the cliffs rise up to 100 feet above the valley floor and have abundant concretions of the iron oxide minerals hematite and limonite. Large tilted layers in the canyon walls are cross-beds formed by the movement of sand grains in river channels or coastal environments. Approximately 318 to 300 million years ago, great rivers carried sand, mud, and silt toward a shallow western sea. As currents pushed these sediments along the channel, sand grains accumulated in piles. When the piles reached an unstable height (known as the angle of repose), grains fell down the steep side of the pile to form a thin layer. Over time these layers accumulated into parallel laminae called cross-beds, named because they form at an angle that "crosses" the main bed. You can tell which direction the rivers were moving 300 million years by locating the steep inclined side of the bed: the water flowed down the sloping crossbeds.

To visit these impressive grounds, follow W Scout Camp Road south of the small town of Covington, and park in the nature preserve lot by the North Trailhead. The moderately rugged 0.8-mile-long North Trail leads down into the canyon, passes through the arch, and climbs to the top of the backbone ridge before looping back to the parking area. The less-traveled South Trail follows the shallow reaches of the upper canyon on a 1.1-mile-long trek.

Among the sharp curves and floodplains of Bear Creek, a narrow 100-foot-tall backbone ridge extends up the stream valley.

A small tributary stream of Bear Creek carved an opening through the massive Mansfield sandstone layers to create the Portland Arch. Note the large cross-beds on the right side of the arch. —Courtesy of Lee Mandrell, Leman's Studios

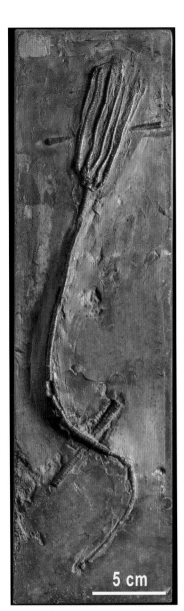

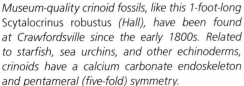

15 SUGAR CREEK TRAIL
Crawfordsville Crinoids
40.0386, -86.9589

Some of the world's best crinoid fossils come from the soft, sandy shale banks of Sugar Creek in Crawfordsville, located in central Montgomery County. The remarkably intact echinoderm fossils found here are displayed in museums and collections around the globe and have made Indiana famous for crinoid paleontological research. Preserved in Mississippian-age siltstone, these fossils provide a snapshot of life on the edge of a shallow sea 345 to 340 million years ago.

During the Early to Middle Mississippian Period, water flowed from western Ohio to the eastern Illinois Basin in a large braided river system called the Borden delta. To the east, the Appalachian Mountains were beginning to form in a tectonic collision known as the Acadian Orogeny. Ancient rivers poured off the mountain highlands and carried large quantities of eroded sediment toward the shallow inland sea that covered southern Indiana. As the river delta grew and migrated along the ocean shoreline, fine-grained sand and silt were deposited in a series of overlapping lobes in what would later become the Edwardsville Formation of the Borden Group.

Dense communities of crinoids flourished along the delta margin. Often referred to as "sea lilies" because of their plantlike appearance, these marine animals consisted of a stem anchored to the seafloor, a rigid calyx that enclosed soft body organs, and feathery arms that

Museum-quality crinoid fossils, like this 1-foot-long Scytalocrinus robustus *(Hall), have been found at Crawfordsville since the early 1800s. Related to starfish, sea urchins, and other echinoderms, crinoids have a calcium carbonate endoskeleton and pentameral (five-fold) symmetry.*

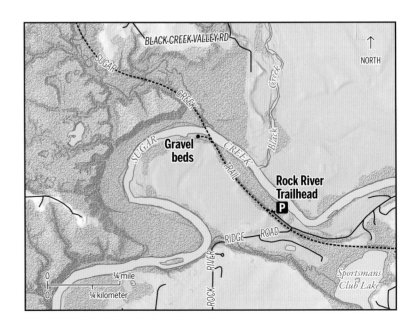

Gravel beds along Sugar Creek contain abundant fragments of crinoid columnals, which can be round, oval, elliptical, pentagonal, or even square in shape. The hole in the center contained a fluid-filled sac and nerve that extended the length of the animal's stem.

filtered food from the water. The stem's flat, stacked columnal disks were held together by ligaments, which decomposed rapidly when the animal died. Most crinoid fossils are found as a hash of scattered columnal segments, locally known as "Indian beads," making the complete specimens found in Crawfordsville truly extraordinary.

The superb preservation of crinoid fossils at Crawfordsville is due to their location on the edge of the Borden delta. Influxes of silt from the fluctuating rivers allowed entire crinoid communities to be buried in situ, preserving complete stem, roots, and calyx in stunning detail. Crinoid species had a diverse range of stem lengths, allowing each to find their own feeding niche in the water column. More than 60 species have been found in the Crawfordsville area, and their well-preserved morphologies have driven much of what is known about the ecology and behavior of ancient crinoids.

While the most abundant fossil sites are closed to the public, Sugar Creek Trail offers an accessible look at the fossil communities that made Crawfordsville famous. From the Rock River Trailhead, walk the easy 0.3-mile paved trail to the pedestrian bridge across the creek. At the southwest end of the bridge, wood steps lead down to a footpath. Follow the path to the gravel bed at the creek, where fragments of crinoids and occasional brachiopods can be found among the river rock.

16 TURKEY RUN STATE PARK
Cool Climates in Carved Canyons
39.8821, -87.2019

More than 11,500 acres of narrow sandstone canyons, vertical bluffs, and winding gorges extend along a 2.5-mile stretch of Sugar Creek at Turkey Run State Park. Located 2 miles north of Marshall in Parke County, the park is Indiana's second-oldest state park, established in 1916. Known for its challenging terrain, the park owes its rugged topography to glacial meltwater that scoured ancient bedrock at the end of the most recent ice age to form an unusual part of the Central Wabash Valley. The cliffs maintain a cooler temperature year-round, providing an ideal habitat for mosses and trees that are more typical in northern climates.

The steep cliffs and deep canyons at Turkey Run are composed of coarse-grained, cross-bedded sandstone belonging to the Mansfield Formation. Layers of sand were deposited in the channels of braided rivers that flowed across a tropical marsh in the Early Pennsylvanian Period. The currents shifted back and forth over the landscape, and lush trees grew in the swampy waters. Shifting currents produced inclined cross-beds, which you can see on the canyon walls, and plant material accumulated to form the thin seam of coal exposed above Sugar Creek near the junction of Trails 4 and 8.

Approximately 21,000 years ago, during the Wisconsin Stage of glaciation, ice sheets began to retreat northward and meltwater poured across the till plains, carving the Wabash Valley into the sandstone below. As the Wabash River became entrenched in its deepening valley, Sugar Creek and other tributaries were forced to cut to lower depths. Unlike softer strata that erodes into broad, shallow valleys, the hard, resistant layers of Mansfield sandstone resisted erosion, and the powerful currents scoured narrow, rock-walled gorges between drift-covered uplands. The park canyon known as Rocky Hollow is an excellent example of a deeply incised tributary, and you can see where the stream cut the nearly vertical canyon walls.

Wedge Rock, located on Trail 3 in Rocky Hollow, is a remnant piece of sandstone that broke off the canyon walls because of freeze-thaw action in the jointed sandstone.

Sugar Creek continues to erode and undercut sandstone along the outer reaches of the stream valley.

It is easy to feel dwarfed by the tall sandstone exposures of the Mansfield Formation in Rocky Hollow.

To see the bold exposures of sandstone for yourself, take Trail 1 from Turkey Run Inn to the suspension bridge. Continue east for a moderate stroll through box canyons and along cliff edges, or cross Sugar Creek for more challenging excursions through Rocky Hollow—Falls Canyon Nature Preserve. Follow Trail 3 up Rocky Hollow and scramble over moss-covered ravines to the Punch Bowl, a large pothole abraded by glacial erratics. From here, you can continue on Trail 10 to the uplands for a scenic view from the Camel's Back, or turn back toward the Ice Box and Falls Canyon. The most daring visitors will want to leave time for the Ladders between Trails 3 and 5, where a series of wooden stepladders bridge the steep walls between Rocky and Bear Hollows. Portions of these trails may be impassible during high water, and visitors should be mindful of muddy, uneven terrain throughout the park.

17 SHADES STATE PARK
Shades of Death on an Unconformity
39.9253, -87.0718

Shades State Park is a hidden gem of the Indiana State Park system. Located 4 miles north of Waveland in Montgomery County, this quiet neighbor of Turkey Run is a favorite for geology enthusiasts who prefer a secluded natural setting. The park's looming sandstone cliffs cast a perpetual twilight over the virgin hardwood forest, which led to the park's original nickname, Shades of Death. Today, the timeworn ravines and waterfalls provide insights into the effects of the last ice age on the Tipton Till Plain.

The vertical bluffs and rocky canyons at Shades were formed by the rapid incision of Sugar Creek and its tributaries approximately 21,000 years ago, when swift currents of glacial meltwater cut through the hard sandstone strata to form narrow, rock-walled gorges. Two different stratigraphic units make up the rugged landscape seen here. The massive cliffs in the upland areas are composed of iron-rich sandstone from the Pennsylvanian-age Mansfield Formation, while the undercut foundations of bluffs and streams are made of shale and siltstone of the Mississippian-age Borden Group. The younger sandstone was deposited on an eroded surface of the older Mississippian rock. The contact between the two is called an unconformity, a region-wide feature reflecting the massive erosional event that scoured bedrock across the state prior to the deposition of the Mansfield Formation. You can see the sharply contrasting units along the cliff faces and ravines south of Sugar Creek.

The rocky hollows at Shades State Park, as well as at Pine Hills Nature Preserve on the park's east side, are lushly forested. Groves of white pine and hemlock, typically found in cooler northern climates, are remnants of ice age vegetation that once flourished throughout central Indiana. To experience the scenery close up, take Trail 1 to Devil's Punch Bowl, a moss-covered grotto with seeping springs carved in Mansfield sandstone, before continuing east through a smooth, slippery streambed to Silver Cascade. This gently tumbling waterfall has a unique convex shape as a result of freezing and thawing within siltstone and shale of the Borden Group. As water travels through the porous rock, it freezes and expands to produce the unusual bulging shape. From the falls, continue up to Inspiration and Prospect Points for unparalleled

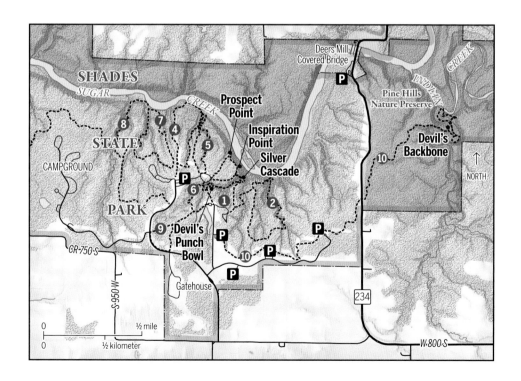

Colorful iron-rich layers known as Liesegang rings occur in the massive ledges of Mansfield sandstone.

The foreboding shadows within the park's ravines inspired the pioneer nickname Shades of Death.

Water gently rolls over Silver Cascade, whose unique convex shape is due to freeze-thaw action. The thin ledges of limestone from the Borden Group above the falls contain abundant crinoid fossils.

The narrow backbone ridges at Pine Hills Nature Preserve form some of the most remarkable examples of incised meanders in the eastern United States.

views of the entrenched valley along Sugar Creek 210 feet below. Follow Trails 4 and 5 for ladder climbs through narrow ravines or continue east on Trail 10 to reach Pine Hills Nature Preserve. Added in 1969 as the state's first nature preserve, Pine Hills boasts challenging trails through four steep, narrow ridges, or backbones. Drastically undercut by the persistent force of meandering streams, the backbones are composed mostly of siltstone from the Borden Group and range from 70 to 125 feet in height and 400 to 1,000 feet in length. The most spectacular is the Devil's Backbone, whose flat 6-foot-wide top is often mistaken for a man-made structure. Carvings of passenger pigeons and the Devil himself were etched into the sandy structure in the 1800s, but as with all state properties, please take only photographs and leave only footprints.

18 INDIANA STATE MUSEUM
Natural History on Display
39.7684, -86.1694

From crinoid-bearing slabs from Crawfordsville to abundant Brookville brachiopods, and from curious Kentland shatter cones to peculiar peccaries from Indiana Caverns, the Indiana State Museum's collections preserve the finest specimens—a treat for those of us who love geology. Exhibits showcase the environments and organisms that called Indiana home during the past 480 million years, with more than 452,000 artifacts and specimens housed in the museum.

The museum's expansive collections are rooted in Indiana's history of scientific research. In the late nineteenth century, interest in science was spurred by an emerging knowledge of Darwin's theories and the debate between science and religion. In 1869, after the Civil War, the Indiana General Assembly passed an act to "provide for a geological survey, and for the collection and preservation of a geological and mineralogical cabinet of the natural history of this State." The state appointed Edward T. Cox, Indiana's fourth State Geologist, to curate and organize thousands of rock, mineral, and fossil specimens collected from Indiana and the surrounding Midwest.

To visit the Indiana State Museum, park in the underground garage at White River State Park in Indianapolis and enter on the first floor. The natural history galleries are located on this bottom level and highlight the evolution of Earth, ancient life-forms, and ongoing investigations into the natural world. The Ancient Seas gallery tells the story of Indiana's geologic history

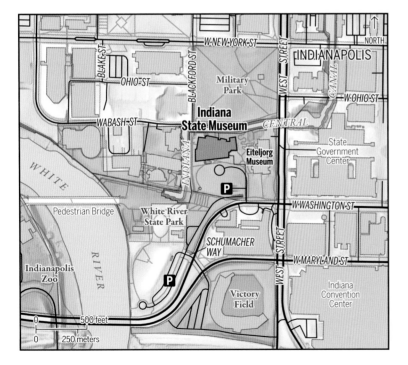

Sculptures representing each of Indiana's 92 counties are showcased on the museum's limestone exterior.

through fossil evidence. The hands-on interactive exhibits display a remarkable array of specimens from the state's best fossil sites. A life-sized limestone quarry diorama is located directly above the fossil cases. On the second floor, Stone Belt workers are shown quarrying stone next to a large overlook of the Indianapolis skyline, emphasizing that Indiana's fossiliferous bedrock is the foundation of our modern cityscapes. Take a trip back to the Pleistocene Epoch in the Frozen Reign gallery, where you can see complete skeletons of mastodons, mammoths, saber-toothed cats, and other ice age mammals. Cultural history exhibits are located on the second floor, and rotating exhibits on science, art, and history topics are on the third floor.

The limestone quarry diorama on the second floor overlooks the Indianapolis skyline and natural history gallery.

Walk, bike, or kayak along the Indiana Central Canal behind the Indiana State Museum.

19 TRENTON FIELD
Oil and Gas Giant
40.3427, -85.3498

Hidden under the Central Till Plain lies one of the earliest and largest oil and natural gas fields in North America. First discovered in 1876, the Trenton Field was once home to a sea of derricks and gas flares that more closely resembled Dante's Inferno than the quiet farm fields seen today. From 1886 to 1913, oil and natural gas flowed abundantly from the Ordovician-age bedrock in east-central Indiana. During its 25-year boom, the Trenton Field was the largest natural gas field known in the world, and its development transformed the economic and social history of the region.

Prior to the mid-nineteenth century, wood, coal, and whale oil were America's fuels of choice. Driven by rising prices and an increasingly industrial economy, inventors began exploring hydrocarbon energy sources. The first success came in 1859, when a rudimentary drill rig struck oil in northwestern Pennsylvania. Soon speculators moved west to Ohio and Indiana, and a few small wells were drilled and abandoned between 1862 and 1869. In 1876, a 600-foot-deep well in Eaton, Indiana, produced enough natural gas to spark a 2-foot flame that burned for 10 years. Despite the abundant quantities of gas, most regarded this initial discovery as a curiosity, and the well was abandoned for coal and petroleum prospects.

The tide turned, however, in 1886 when the Eaton well was deepened to 922 feet in the Trenton Limestone to produce the first commercially successful gas well. Nearby wells began producing both oil and gas, and the Trenton Field's potential sparked the country's attention. Soon, hundreds of gas wells sprung up between Findlay, Ohio, and Portland, Indiana. The cities of Muncie, Anderson, and Kokomo advertised their ample supply of cheap fuel, and over 100 glass factories, ceramic plants, and tin-plate mills moved into the area. As the gas boom continued, communities took great pride in their so-called unlimited supply and often burned flares day and night for months on end. Derricks, burning wells, and pipelines covered the landscape, and production peaked in

1900 with more than 35 billion cubic feet of gas produced in a single year.

The Trenton Field's oil and gas boom ended as quickly as it began. By 1902, unregulated drilling practices had turned the reservoir's overlying seal into Swiss cheese, and wellhead pressure began to drop. Natural gas in the Trenton Limestone was rapidly depleted, and the state began to import resources by 1913. Today, places like Gas City serve as distant reminders of the Trenton Field's storied past, though a few wells still produce small quantities of oil and gas. You can visit the site of Indiana's first gas well at Norsemen Park in downtown Eaton, located about 12 miles north of Muncie.

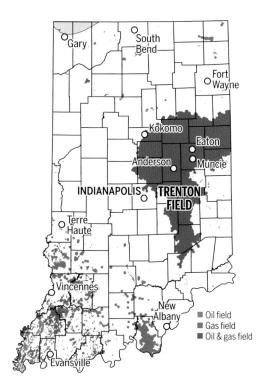

"Shooting the well" near Bryant, Jay County, in 1890. Note the nitroglycerin wagon in the center foreground.

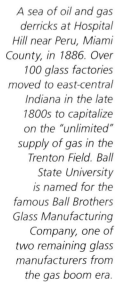

A sea of oil and gas derricks at Hospital Hill near Peru, Miami County, in 1886. Over 100 glass factories moved to east-central Indiana in the late 1800s to capitalize on the "unlimited" supply of gas in the Trenton Field. Ball State University is named for the famous Ball Brothers Glass Manufacturing Company, one of two remaining glass manufacturers from the gas boom era.

20 WHITEWATER VALLEY GORGE PARK
Falls Diverted over Fossiliferous Rock
39.8480, -84.8989

Approximately 451 to 444 million years ago, a flurry of marine animals invaded a shallow ocean that covered much of the North American continent, an event known as the Richmondian Invasion. A variety of nonnative species from basins to the east and northwest traveled freely into Indiana's warm tropical waters when sea level rose at the end of the Ordovician Period. Similar to the modern invasion of zebra mussels in the Great Lakes, species of brachiopods, corals, and cephalopods invaded Indiana, Ohio, and Kentucky, producing some of the most fossil-rich beds in the world. The fossiliferous layers are part of the Whitewater Formation, some of the oldest strata exposed in Indiana. An impressive array of these fossils is preserved in rocks of the Cincinnati Arch along Indiana's southeastern boundary. One of the best places to explore this unique geological period is Whitewater Valley Gorge Park, a natural area in the heart of the city of Richmond. Here, in a region where rocks are mostly hidden beneath the eastwardly thinning glacial drift of the New Castle Till Plains, you can walk beside fossiliferous cliffs, waterfalls, and historic structures.

The scenic 3.5-mile byway follows the gorge from Industries Road to Test Road. The wooded path is moderately difficult, and four parking areas provide easy access points to the trail. Park at the Springwood Lake lot to reach Thistlethwaite Falls, a 10-foot-high waterfall that tumbles down thinly bedded, clay-rich limestone and calcareous shale from the Whitewater Formation. The falls were created in 1854 when early settlers dammed the East Fork of the Whitewater River, forcing the river to flow over the rock ledge so they could use the waterpower for manufacturing mills. From the falls, follow a sandy trail downstream to steep shaly limestone bluffs. Abundant fossils occur along the base of the bluffs, but please do not remove fossils from the walls of the gorge. You may collect loose fossils, including brachiopods, corals, and trilobites,

from the stream banks or rubble piles located at the bottom of slopes and along roadsides. Pick up a free fossil pamphlet at the Old National Road Welcome Center or Joseph Moore Museum on the nearby campus of Earlham College.

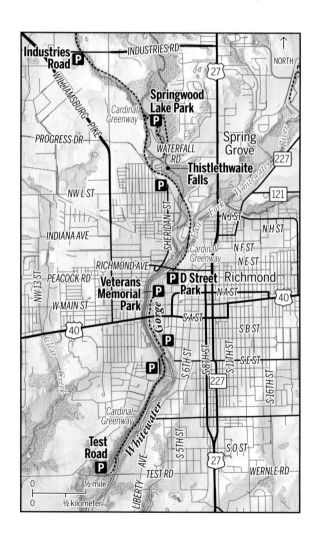

52

Whitewater Valley Gorge was incised by three converging branches of the Whitewater River during the Wisconsin Stage of glaciation.

Water cascades over bluish-gray rubbly limestone and interbedded calcareous shale of the Whitewater Formation at Thistlethwaite Falls.

21 BROOKVILLE LAKE DAM
Storm Deposits at the Spillway
39.4385, -84.9950

An enormous cut through Late Ordovician strata in the New Castle Till Plains occurs within the spillway at Brookville Lake. Located about 2 miles north of downtown Brookville in Franklin County, the 180-foot-high exposure on the lake's southwestern shore displays an astonishing concentration of fossils within the shale and limestone beds of the Dillsboro Formation. In 1975 the US Army Corps of Engineers dammed the East Fork of the Whitewater River to control floods, and the spillway excavation revealed some of the richest fossil deposits in the world.

Like Whitewater Valley Gorge, Versailles State Park, and Clifty Falls State Park, the rocks at Brookville Lake were deposited 451 to 444 million years ago during an event known as the Richmondian Invasion. New species were introduced to the warm tropical seas that covered southeastern Indiana, and westward-blowing winds swept across the area and churned the shallow waters, leaving jumbled mixtures of shells, skeletons, and silt. When the waters calmed, fine-grained mud settled to the seafloor until the next storm. These storm deposits, called tempestites, are within the Dillsboro Formation, and their alternating layers can be traced along outcrops in Indiana, Ohio, and Kentucky.

Alternating layers of blue-gray shale and gray limestone are evident in the massive spillway cut located directly west of the dam. The amount of limestone gradually increases toward the upper half of the outcrop. The lowest 22 feet of the cut is composed of thick shale units with interbedded thin fossiliferous limestone beds. Above this section lies 30 feet of coarse, poorly bedded limestone with fragmented shell debris. The overlying 90 feet are a mix of blocky to fissile shale and limestone, with a prominent 10-foot-thick limestone band stretching across the outcrop about 70 feet up. A second protruding limestone band is evident about 145 feet up, and the top 40 feet of the outcrop consists of shale with limestone beds. To visit the Brookville Lake Dam tempestites, turn north from IN 101 into the Dam and Tailwater Area on the south side of the dam. Park in the small lot, and walk a half mile along the top of the dam to reach the looming rock exposure.

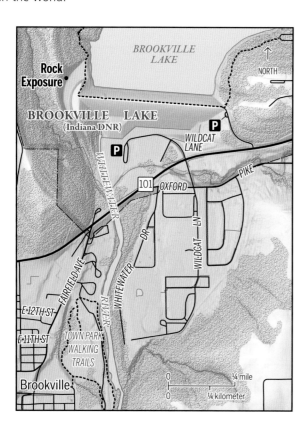

An overlook on the east side of Brookville Lake provides a view of the dam and adjacent outcrop.

The alternating shale and limestone beds of the west side of the Brookville Lake Dam spillway formed in a shallow sea that was located 15 to 20 degrees south of the equator during the Late Ordovician Period.

Fossilized brachiopods, bryozoans, horn corals, and trilobites weather out of tempestites in the Dillsboro Formation.

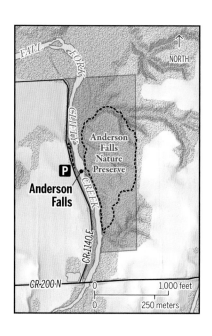

##
22 ANDERSON FALLS
Indiana's Niagara Falls
39.2372, -85.6994

Anderson Falls in Bartholomew County is a miniature version of Niagara Falls. Located about 14 miles east of Columbus, the Fall Fork of Clifty Creek cascades over a 100-foot-wide bedrock ledge in the middle of the New Castle Till Plains. While significantly smaller than its New York counterpart, Anderson Falls provides a near-scale model of the geological processes at work in Niagara Falls and offers a welcome escape from the flat agricultural fields and residential areas that surround the region.

The rock-walled valley and waterfall at Anderson Falls are the result of differential erosion involving two bedrock formations. The lip of the falls is composed of erosion-resistant Geneva Dolomite of the Devonian-age Jeffersonville Limestone, and the underlying plunge pool is made of Silurian-age Waldron Shale. Just as the Niagara River eroded Silurian shale underlying dolostone to form Niagara Falls, the

The Fall Fork of Clifty Creek streams over a lip of Geneva Dolomite to the less-resistant Waldron Shale below. —Courtesy of Lee Mandrell, Leman's Studios

A 1-mile trail loops through the woods on the east bank of the Fall Fork of Clifty Creek. Be cautious of stream currents and slippery bedrock when crossing the river to reach the park trails.

Fall Fork of Clifty Creek has undercut the soft, thinly bedded shale and limestone below a dolostone ledge to form Anderson Falls. Each time the dolomite ledge becomes unstable, large slabs break off and fall into the plunge pool below, moving the falls further upstream.

The 14-foot drop over the falls is the focal point of a 44-acre county park. To visit, park in the small lot on CR 1140 E, and walk across the road to an overlook platform. From here, follow the footpath upstream past the falls. When water levels are low and the limestone bedrock is exposed, you can carefully cross over the creek to the east bank and follow wooded trails through shaded ravines, floodplains, and streamside bluffs. Exposures of the Waldron Shale below the falls are full of fossils, but collecting is not permitted.

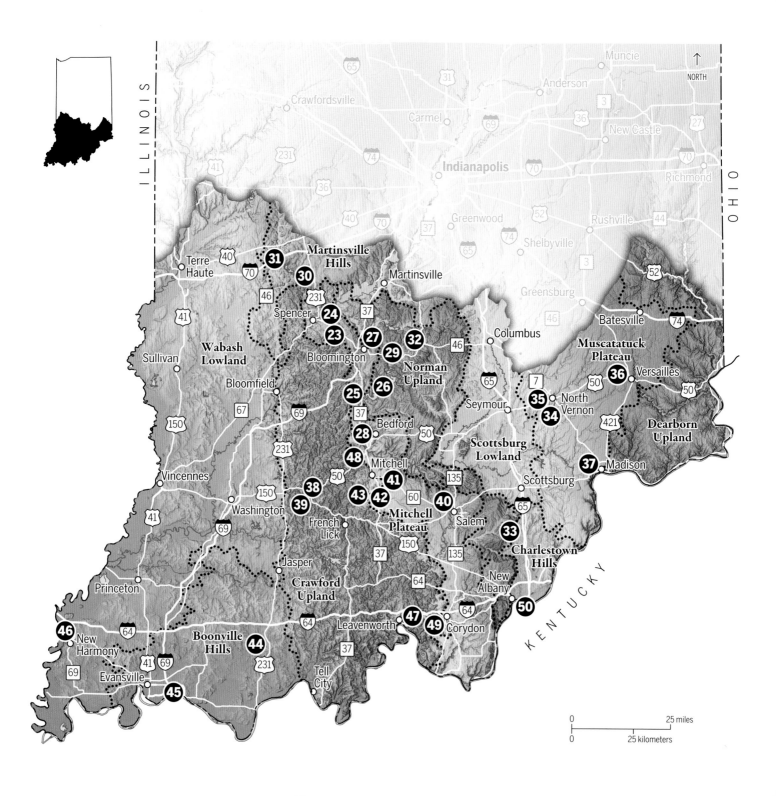

Southern Hills and Lowlands Region

Characterized by rugged uplands, dendritic valleys, and entrenched streams, the Southern Hills and Lowlands Region stands in stark contrast to the till-covered plains to the north. While it is located south of the southern limit of the Wisconsin Stage of glaciation, nearly three-fifths of the region was covered by ice during the Pre-Illinoian and Illinoian Stages of glaciation. The White, Wabash, and Ohio Rivers each carried huge volumes of glacial meltwater that carved the valleys significantly deeper than the modern flows could have, and outwash sand was blown into dunes and loess along the Wabash and Scottsburg Lowlands. Bedrock in this region is progressively younger toward the southwest, reflecting the relative dip of rock layers as they descend into the Illinois Basin.

Ordovician-age rocks along the Dearborn Upland preserve some of the oldest fossil exposures in the state, while Pennsylvanian-age sandstones and coals in the Wabash Lowland reflect the vast swamp forests that once thrived along an ocean's edge. Thick layers of Devonian and Mississippian limestone along the Muscatatuck Plateau, Mitchell Plateau, and Crawford Upland erode readily to form sinkholes, karst valleys, and caves, and the Knobstone Escarpment runs through the center of the region to form a striking topographic backbone.

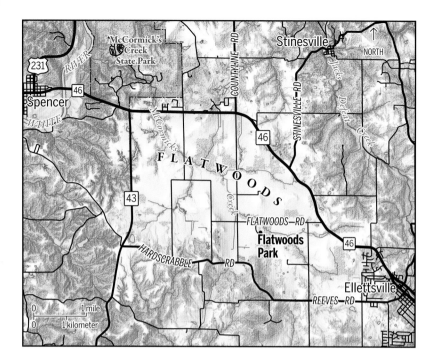

23 FLATWOODS PARK
Glacial Lake Drained by Underground Streams
39.2525, -86.6777

Driving south on IN 46 between Spencer and Ellettsville, you could easily pass by a unique feature known as Glacial Lake Flatwoods. This somewhat flat, low-level basin is a former lake bottom within the Mitchell Plateau, a hilly terrain where carbonate bedrock typically controls the topography.

Surrounded by hills and ridges composed of Mississippian-age limestone, the Flatwoods region is an ancient lakebed that measures 6 miles long and about 2 miles wide. McCormicks Creek runs through the region's long axis, flowing northeast to meet the White River at McCormick's Creek State Park. The flat plain has several sinkholes that divert surface streams underground through sub-terranean passageways, and the water resurfaces as springs along nearby streams.

When the margin of the ice sheet stagnated near what is today the state park during the Illi-noian Stage of glaciation, meltwater streamed into the area and buried the former land surface with sand, silt, and clay. Glacial ice crossed the White River and blocked stream outlets, causing meltwa-ter and new drainageways to gather in front of the ice sheet and form Glacial Lake Flatwoods. After the ice retreated, water escaped through low gaps, and shallow sinks began draining the northeast portion of the lake. McCormicks Creek continued to drain the lake through its underground network, leaving behind a flat lake plain. Flatwoods Park, a county park, lies in the south-central part of the ancient lakebed. An easy half-mile trail features interpretive signs about the flora, hydrology, and geology of the park.

Near the entrance to Flatwoods Park, the flat nature of the glacial lakebed is easily contrasted against the surrounding hills of Mississippian bedrock.

60

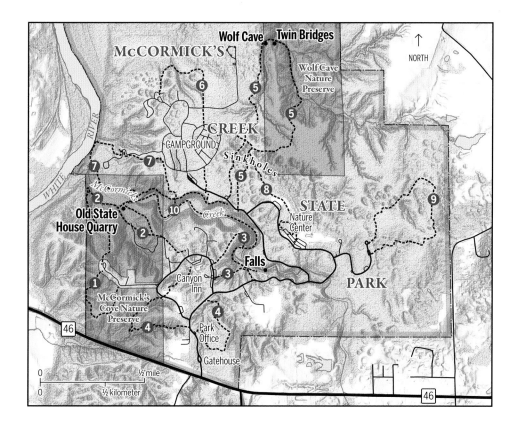

24 MCCORMICK'S CREEK STATE PARK
Limestone Canyon, Quarry, and Caves
39.2835, -86.7262

Named after the first settler in the area, McCormick's Creek State Park was Indiana's first state park, dedicated on July 4, 1916. Located 2 miles east of Spencer, its rolling hills, steep-walled valleys, and limestone-solution features are characteristic of the Mitchell Plateau. The focal point of the park is the mile-long McCormicks Creek canyon, where water tumbles through a steep-walled limestone valley on its way to the White River.

The Salem Limestone occurs at the base of the canyon. Thick-bedded and uniform in texture, this stone has been quarried extensively for dimension (building) stone in the south-central Indiana Stone Belt region. Near the junction of Trails 2 and 7,

you can see the massive weathered blocks and quarried ledges of the Old State House Quarry, which produced stone for the construction of the State Capitol building in Indianapolis between 1878 and 1880. The St. Louis Limestone, a fine-grained, thin-bedded carbonate with layers of shale, dolomite, and occasional chert nodules, composes the middle portion of the canyon walls above the Salem. A short walk on Trail 3 leads to McCormicks Creek Falls, which cascades over a resistant lip of St. Louis Limestone. The fine-grained, smooth-textured Ste. Genevieve Limestone constitutes the upper 50 feet of the canyon. All three formations are from the middle of

Cross-beds along a weathered joint in the Salem Limestone at the Old State House Quarry.

McCormicks Creek plunges through a limestone canyon to join the White River.

Entrance to Twin Bridges near Wolf Cave along Trail 5. —Courtesy of Lee Mandrell, Leman's Studios

the Mississippian Period, together representing about 1 million years of geologic history.

The canyon first formed during the Illinoian Stage of glaciation, when ice blocked preglacial valleys and new drainage patterns were cut into the underlying limestone bedrock. Beginning at the White River, McCormicks Creek has eroded the bedrock far upstream to create the canyon seen today. Sinkholes dot the landscape north and south of the canyon. This karst topography, a result of more recent erosion on the carbonate bedrock, is best seen inside Wolf Cave Nature Preserve. A 2-mile loop on Trail 5 passes Wolf Cave and Twin Bridges, both remnants of collapsed caves that were exposed through erosion. Visitors can climb through the smooth, dry passageway of Wolf Cave, but be aware that the width is limited to 20 inches in some places.

25 CEDAR BLUFFS NATURE PRESERVE
Wilderness in the Stone Belt
39.0353, -86.5676

The steep bluffs, fallen boulders, and gnarled cedar trees in a hidden corner of southwestern Monroe County may have you doubting that you're in Indiana. High above the limestone quarries and karst terrain of the surrounding countryside, you can hike along carbonate cliffs for a scenic escape at Cedar Bluffs Nature Preserve.

The nature preserve lies within the western extent of the Mitchell Plateau. Surrounded by rolling limestone terrain, the 75-foot-high bluffs extend along the northern bank of Clear Creek and are composed of two units of Mississippian-age limestone. The Harrodsburg Limestone occurs in the lower half of the bluffs, and its thin, cross-bedded limestone layers weather rapidly to form the sheer slope along the creek shoreline. The upper 20 feet is made up of the Salem Limestone, whose massive beds cap the ridge. Fragments of fossilized crinoids and bryozoans are visible in both units, and water trickles out at seeps along the contact between the two limestone formations.

The 1-mile trail is challenging with rocky, uneven terrain and occasional low clearance. To visit, park on the north side of South Ketcham Road and walk along a short, narrow trail through the woods to the banks of Clear Creek. The marked trail ends here, and you must scramble downstream across the rocky shoreline to where the bluffs come to a point. Turn left, and follow a footpath up the back side of the steep bluffs. At the top, wander through the stand of red cedar trees that gives the property its name. The view from the top of the limestone bluffs reveals a wooded landscape that feels like true wilderness in the Mitchell Plateau.

Looking out from the bluff overlook, a distant ridge is visible about 1.5 miles to the west. This high point is part of the Springville Escarpment, and it marks the boundary between the Mitchell Plateau and Crawford Upland. —Courtesy of Steven Higgs, Natural Bloomington

The massive nature of the Salem Limestone is visible in the upper portion of Cedar Bluffs. Known locally as "Indiana limestone," the Salem is quarried as a world-class dimension (building) stone in several quarries nearby.

The path to the limestone bluffs winds along the rocky southern shore of Clear Creek.

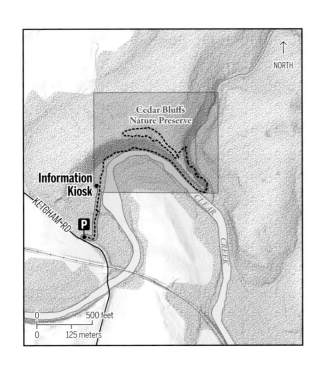

65

26 MONROE LAKE
Crinoid Communities on a Limestone Penninsula
39.0312, -86.4459

You'll find no better place than Monroe Lake to search for the donut-shaped, platelike stem sections of fossil crinoids. The remains of ancient echinoderm animals, these columnals, or "Indian beads," are the most common and easily recognized parts of fossil crinoids, and they can be found in a variety of sizes. For the past 50 years, researchers at Indiana University have studied the fossil populations here. More than 200 species have been identified from Monroe Lake's fossiliferous banks, making the area a prime location for examining the ancient communities that inhabited the Borden delta 345 to 340 million years ago.

Rocks at Monroe Lake belong to the Edwardsville Formation of the Borden Group. Similar to those in Crawfordsville, Brown County, and the Knobstone Escarpment, exposures of the Borden Group at Monroe Lake are the remains of an ancient river delta that crossed Indiana in the early to middle part of the Mississippian Period. As rivers flowed west into the Illinois Basin sediments were deposited in a series of intertwined lobes and over time formed into the Edwardsville Formation.

The shallow waters of the Borden delta had varying depositional conditions. Tides, water depth, and sediment suspension affected deposition, and organisms in these settings adapted to the special environment in which they lived. Similar to the tiered zones of trees and shrubs in modern forests, fossil communities were also separate and distinct. Long-stemmed crinoids, sponges, and tall bryozoans fed high in the water column, and brachiopods and trilobites flourished near the bottom.

One of the best places to view these fossil communities is at Allens Creek State Recreation Area. Located 11 miles south of Bloomington, the wooded peninsula juts out of Monroe Lake's southern shoreline to expose 81 unique species of crinoids, bryozoans, brachiopods, and corals in interbedded limestone and siltstone bedrock. The limestone displays varying degrees of silicification, and geodes are present on some of the bedding surfaces. Crinoids at Allens Creek are mostly broken apart into columnals, though some still-attached stems can be found. A moderate 1.75-mile nonlooping trail leads down the peninsula to exposed fossil beds with a serene lake view. This site is state property, so fossil collecting is not allowed.

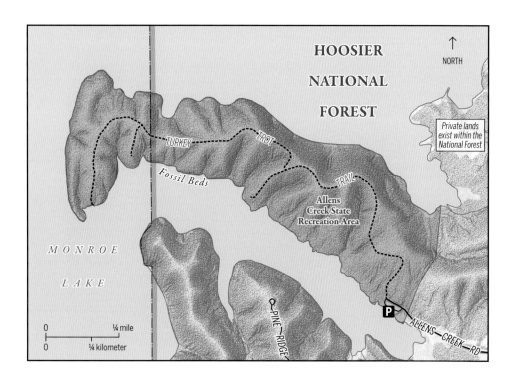

66

Fossil hash of crinoid columnal, bryozoan, and brachiopod fossils within the Edwardsville Formation.

Several crinoid species collected from Monroe Lake, such as Nipterocrinus monroensis shown here, are only known to occur in this locality.

Five distinct biological zones occur within 2.5 miles along the Monroe Lake shoreline. The unique fossils that lived in these zones provide evidence that environmental differences controlled organism distribution.

27 INDIANA UNIVERSITY CAMPUS
Artistry in Salem Limestone
39.1665, -86.5266

What do the Empire State Building, the Pentagon, and Indiana University's Sample Gates all have in common? The answer may surprise you. All these structures are made of "Indiana limestone," a colloquial and trade term for the Salem Limestone that is quarried extensively in the Indiana Stone Belt. Running from Owen County southeast through Monroe and Lawrence Counties and into northwest Washington County, the 30-mile-long outcrop belt has supplied 50 to 75 percent of all limestone used in North American buildings.

The Salem Limestone is part of a thick carbonate sequence that formed on the shelf of a shallow tropical sea 358 to 323 million years ago in the Middle Mississippian Period. Even-textured and massive in outcrop, the gray-to-tan-colored stone is characterized by the uniformity of its rounded, sand-sized grains of fossil fragments. Nearshore wave and tidal currents sorted the remains of bryozoans and echinoderms into a consistent size, giving the limestone its smooth texture, which makes it a favorite of carvers and architects. The Salem is classified as a "freestone" because its massive and uniform character allows it to be sawed or carved in any direction. Large pieces can be sculpted from its thick beds.

Twelve limestone owls, ranging from 2 inches to 5 feet in height, are scattered on the exteriors of various buildings, making them the most common carved figure on campus. The owl is a symbol of wisdom and knowledge throughout the Western world.

Nowhere is the beauty and durability of Salem Limestone better demonstrated than the Bloomington campus of Indiana University. Located in the northeastern part of the city, it has been called one of the most beautiful college campuses in the country. Spanning more than 100 years of construction history, the Italianate, Romanesque, Gothic Revival, Art Deco, and Modern buildings boast stylized lettering, dramatic entryways, and spectacular sculptures. An easy 1-mile walking tour led by the Indiana Geological and Water Survey explores these grand structures in the heart of the Stone Belt.

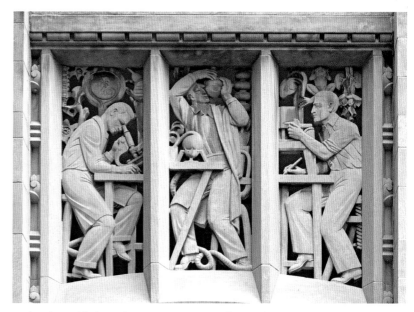

The three-sided south tower at Myers Hall is perhaps the most magnificent limestone building entryway at Indiana University. The carved limestone frieze depicts an anatomist, a pharmacologist, and a physiologist in stunning detail.

Gothic Revival pointed arches and buttresses at the Sample Gates welcome visitors to the Indiana University Bloomington campus.

28 LAND OF LIMESTONE MUSEUM
The Nation's Building Stone
38.8752, -86.4830

Salem Limestone has earned the nickname the "Nation's Building Stone" for its impact on the architectural and social history of the United States. First quarried in 1827, it has dominated the national market as a premier building stone for almost two centuries. Clues to the Salem Limestone's storied past are hard to miss. Stone-clad homes, churches, and courthouses grace every town in the state, and water-filled quarries and massive limestone ledges surround you in the drive along the Stone Belt from Bloomington to Bedford.

The earliest quarry operations for Salem Limestone used a star drill and black powder to excavate stone from natural outcrops and riverbanks. Immensely labor intensive, these early efforts were limited to use in bridge abutments and building foundations. The industry grew, however, as transportation and technology advanced. In 1854, the New Albany & Salem Railroad (later called the Monon) was completed, connecting buyers from the Great Lakes, the Ohio River, and beyond. Seventeen years later, when much of Chicago burned to the ground in the Great Fire, the stone industry capitalized on the disaster by promoting the safety and durability of stone construction. The final advancement came in 1875, when steam-powered technology was introduced to the Stone Belt. Steam-powered channeling machines chiseled immense blocks of stone out of the ground at a rate faster than previously possible. With increased production, good transportation, and a thriving national market, the demand for Indiana limestone skyrocketed. At the height of its production in 1929, 12 million cubic feet (300,000 tons) of Salem Limestone was quarried from the Indiana Stone Belt. While today's quarrying techniques and architectural trends have changed, the Indiana Stone Belt industry is alive and well, producing an average of 2.7 million cubic feet (67,500 tons) of dimension stone each year.

The Land of Limestone Museum at the StoneGate Arts & Education Center is located in the former headquarters of the Indiana Limestone Company in Bedford. The museum celebrates this humble stone and its use throughout the world as a premier building material. More than two hundred archival and architectural photographs, historical news accounts, and carved artwork pieces are displayed in the museum's homespun exhibits. The crown jewel of the museum is the building it resides in; entirely clad in limestone, it may be your only chance to climb a stairwell made entirely of Salem Limestone and is a must-see for anyone interested in Indiana's limestone legacy.

The Land of Limestone Museum is located inside the StoneGate Arts & Education Center, which was the former headquarters of the Indiana Limestone Company. —Long Studio, courtesy of the Indiana Limestone Photograph

Intricately carved limestone clads every surface of the Classical Revival–style building built in 1927.

Stained glass medallions manufactured by the Blenko Glass Works portray stone hookers, carvers, and drillers.

71

29 MOUNT CARMEL FAULT
Shifted Strata at the Surface
38.9555, -86.3689

Many faults lie below the surface of Indiana. From the active Wabash Valley Seismic Zone in southwestern Indiana to the recently discovered Sharpsville Fault south of Kokomo, almost all of these faults occur thousands of feet below the surface, with one notable exception—the Mount Carmel Fault. Extending 50 miles through the Norman Upland, the Mount Carmel Fault offers a rare glimpse at the shaky foundations of the state's seismic history.

The Mount Carmel Fault lies along the eastern margin of the Illinois Basin. One of many similar structural features within the basin, the Mount Carmel is a normal fault that developed during the Mississippian and Pennsylvanian Periods and last moved in the Pleistocene Epoch. Emerging from thick glacial drift in southern Morgan County, the fault trends southeast through Monroe, Lawrence, and Jackson Counties before disappearing below the surface in northwestern Washington County. The fault plane is steeply inclined to the west, and the downthrown block is on the western side of the fracture. Strata on the westward side of the fault have been displaced up to 175 feet and, in some places, form a series of narrow folds that have been cut by the fault plane. The Leesville Anticline is one such fold, where rock layers were upturned and dragged along the fault to produce folded domes that lie 1 to 2 miles west of the Mount Carmel Fault. The southwesterly dipping rocks are truncated by the planar fault surface, producing a natural trap for oil and gas accumulation. The Leesville Anticline has been drilled for hydrocarbon exploration since the 1920s and today is used to store natural gas, extracted elsewhere, underground.

You can observe the Mount Carmel Fault at roadcuts throughout Monroe, Lawrence, and Jackson Counties, as well as outcrops in the Charles C. Deam Wilderness. Many exposures offer excellent views of displaced rock units, angular fragments, and disturbed bedding. In some places, limestone sinkhole plains are juxtaposed against shaly valleys, providing a ready contrast between the upthrown and downthrown sides of one of the most significant exposed geological structures in Indiana.

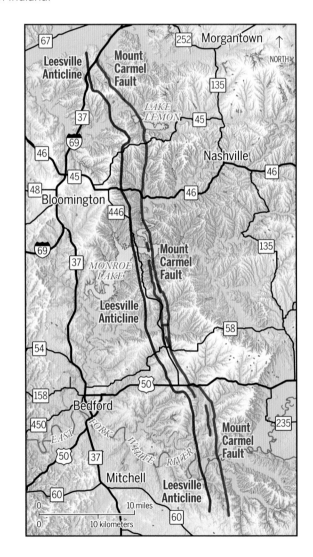

The Mount Carmel Fault juxtaposes sandstone from the Borden Group (left) against Sanders Group limestone (right) at an outcrop south of Fort Ritner in Washington County.

In Monroe County, the Frog Pond Ridge valley in the Charles C. Deam Wilderness parallels the Mount Carmel Fault. The ridge is on the downthrown side of the fault, and its trace is more visible in the autumn and winter after the leaves fall. —Courtesy of Steven Higgs, Natural Bloomington

Massive amounts of water pour over rocky alcoves at Cataract Falls, the largest waterfall by volume in Indiana. Located about 7 miles southwest of Cloverdale in Owen County, the two-tiered cataract is in one of the most beautiful recreation areas in Indiana and is a remnant of the last ice age in the Martinsville Hills region. As Mill Creek flows under the covered bridge and over Upper Cataract Falls, the gentle valley changes into a picturesque gorge.

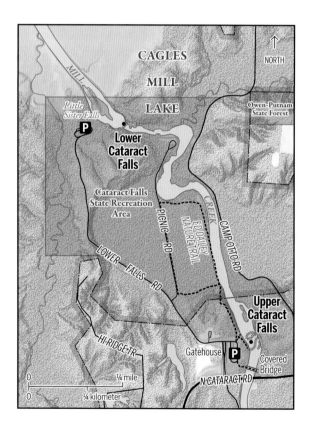

The dramatic cascades at Cataract Falls are the result of meltwater erosion on a glacial lake plain. During the Illinoian Stage of glaciation, thick ice sheets flowed from Canada and stagnated north of the recreation site. As the ice melted, large quantities of meltwater flooded the creek and ponded to form Glacial Lake Quincy. An extensive lake plain developed, and fine-grained silt and clay covered about 40 square miles in northeastern Owen, southeastern Putnam, and western Morgan Counties. When the climate cooled and the ice sheet resumed its retreat northward, Glacial Lake Quincy drained and Mill Creek began to cut across the lake plain, eroding the fine-grained lake sediments to reveal two bedrock ridges below.

More than 100 feet of rock strata is exposed in the waterfalls and gorge at Cataract Falls, providing an excellent stratigraphic column of two Middle Mississippian-age formations. Below the remnants of an old dam at Upper Cataract Falls, Mill Creek cascades over thin beds of the Ste. Genevieve Limestone. At low water levels, large chert nodules of the Indian Creek Beds are exposed directly below the dam. After a few small drops in elevation, water flows over thick-bedded oolitic limestone before plunging about 20 feet over Upper Cataract Falls. The overhang and base of the falls are composed of massive fine-grained calcareous sandstone, which spalls into the plunge pool below. Mill Creek flows about 0.8 mile northwest through the Ste. Genevieve–walled canyon before falling 18 feet at Lower Cataract Falls. The Lost River Chert Bed marks the lip of the U-shaped falls, and the St. Louis Limestone makes up the waterfall base and extensive canyon walls downstream. The contact between the two formations is about 8 feet below the lip of Lower Cataract Falls. Overall, Mill Creek drops more than 80 feet in a 1-mile span. You can explore the canyon and falls on an easy 0.8-mile trail that connects the observation deck at Upper Cataract Falls to Lower Cataract Falls on the western side of Mill Creek.

Water cascades over the Ste. Genevieve Limestone at Upper Cataract Falls.

Below Lower Cataract Falls, Mill Creek intersects a preglacial valley, and there is a noticeable widening of the valley. From here, the creek flows northwest to Cagles Mill Lake within the Lieber State Recreation Area.
—Courtesy of Steven Higgs, Natural Bloomington

31 CAGLES MILL SPILLWAY
Uncovered Unconformity
39.4841, -86.9162

The spillway at Cagles Mill Lake is an extraordinary exposure of Pennsylvanian- and Pleistocene-age strata in the Martinsville Hills. Located about 8 miles southeast of Cloverdale in Putnam County, the spillway was created in 1953 when the US Army Corps of Engineers dammed Mill Creek to create Cagles Mill Lake. Unlike small outcrops nearby, the spillway cuts through a tall ridge to expose rock units typically only seen in the subsurface.

The 1,000-foot-long and 60-foot-deep cut made during the construction of Cagles Mill Lake exposes two river channels

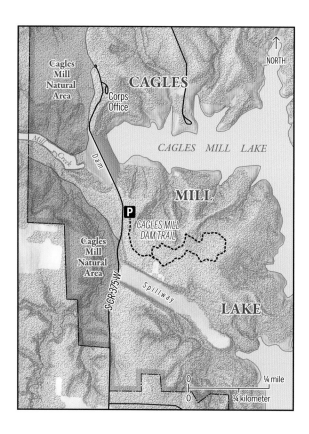

filled with shale, cross-bedded sandstone, and coal from the Pennsylvanian-age Mansfield and Brazil Formations. At the west end of the spillway, beds of gray shale and coal are eroded back to form a low overhang in the bottom 40 feet of the cut. Above this overhang is a yellowish-tan, thinly bedded sandstone channel; cross-bedding and plant impressions are common in the coarse sandy layers, and the sharp contact on the bottom shows evidence of scour in the trough of an ancient stream. The 6-to-53-foot-thick channel curves upward from left to right and cuts through the underlying rocks. In several places, the clay and shaly coal are completely cut out by thick sands of the lower channel.

Near the middle of the spillway exposure, a 0.5-to-3-foot-thick seam of the Lower Block Coal unit curves downward from left to right. The coal is overlain by a black shale that grades upward into a gray shaly sandstone. The sandstone is the upper channel fill and measures up to 23 feet thick. The top of the exposure is 20 feet of thin light-gray sandstone with abundant *Stigmaria* tree root fossils. The change in rock types from bottom to top of the spillway section is the result of a rapidly changing environment approximately 300 million years ago. Layers of decaying vegetation accumulated in the swampy forests, only to be cut out and filled by sandy rivers. As the rivers shifted laterally and sea level fluctuated, sediment deposition changed.

Sediments from the Pleistocene Epoch unconformably overlie Pennsylvanian-age rocks in the east end of the spillway. This exposure, one of best known sections of Pleistocene units in Indiana, provides an excellent record of glacial and interglacial climatic conditions that existed here during the Pleistocene ice age. At the far east end, a thin wedge of lake-deposited clay and fossiliferous loess overlies spalling bedrock. This wedge pinches out to the west and above it lies 27 feet of till and clay from the Pre-Illinoian Stage of glaciation. The uppermost 23 feet is thick till from the Illinoian Stage of glaciation, with a well-developed weather profile that formed during the Sangamon interglacial period. This weathered till was again modified by weathering during the Wisconsin Stage of glaciation. A thin 3-foot cap of Wisconsin loess lies at the top of the ridge.

The Pennsylvanian and Pleistocene strata exposed here provide an outdoor classroom for students of Indiana geology. To visit Cagles Mill Spillway, take IN 42 west toward Poland. Cross the lake and continue east for 8.7 miles before turning right on West Dam Road (County Road 830 W). Follow the gravel road for 2.6 miles, pass the spillway outcrop, and park in the visitors' parking lot on the east side of the road; do not park at the spillway. A short 0.2-mile walk will lead you to the grand bedrock exposures. A park office is 0.6 mile to the north.

On the eastern end of the spillway, brownish silt unconformably covers Pennsylvanian rocks. Filled with fossilized gastropods, this sediment was deposited during the beginning of the Pleistocene Epoch when the land was free of ice and land snails thrived.

Two ancient river channels with shale, cross-bedded sandstone, and coal from the Mansfield Formation are exposed on the northern wall of the spillway.

BROWN COUNTY STATE PARK
Little Smokies
39.1768, -86.2704

Surrounded by relatively flat topography to the north and southeast, the stately hills, ridges, and valleys of Brown County State Park attract more than 1.3 million visitors each year. Nicknamed Indiana's Little Smokies for their resemblance to the Great Smoky Mountains, the undulating hills and valleys were created by the erosive influence of water on Mississippian-age bedrock in the Norman Upland.

Brown County State Park is Indiana's largest park, comprising 16,100 acres with nearly 375 feet of relief. The symmetrical hills and valleys are formed by southwestwardly dipping siltstone, shale, and sandstone belonging to the Edwardsville and Spickert Knob Formations of the Borden Group. These rocks were deposited along the vast Borden delta in the Early to Middle Mississippian Period. In the Early Pennsylvanian Period, a long period of erosion removed hundreds of feet of overlying rock. Freshly exposed, the soft shales of the Spickert Knob were easily worn away to form steep-sided, narrow ravines, and the sandstone layers within the Edwardsville Formation remained as resistant, knobby peaks. Sandstone caps Weed Patch Hill, Hohen Point, and parts of Limekiln Ridge, and each summit rises at least 1,000 feet above sea level. Weed Patch Hill is one of the highest elevations in Indiana and forms the high point of the Knobstone Escarpment at 1,058 feet above sea level.

Although the vast sheets of ice that covered much of Indiana during the Pleistocene Epoch halted north of Nashville, their presence north and east of the park helped to carve the "hills o' Brown" into the grand patterns seen today. Meltwater from the retreating ice masses poured into the local stream valleys and eroded the shaly layers into deep valleys. Ice from the Illinoian Stage of glaciation came closest to the park, and traces of gravel and silt can be found as sediment terraces in Salt Creek near the North Gatehouse.

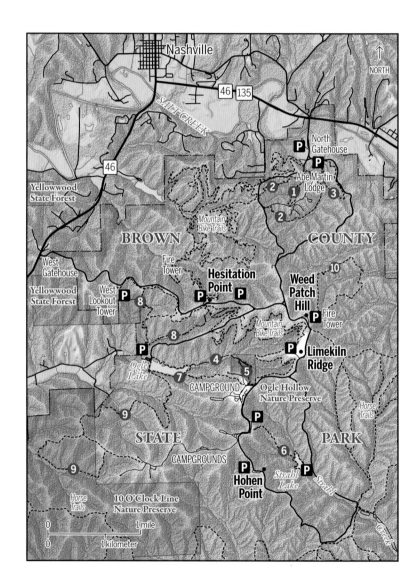

Fossilized remains of crinoids, bryozoans, and brachiopods are visible in bedrock exposures.

Unlike the Great Smoky Mountains, Brown County's rugged topography was created by erosion rather than tectonic collision.

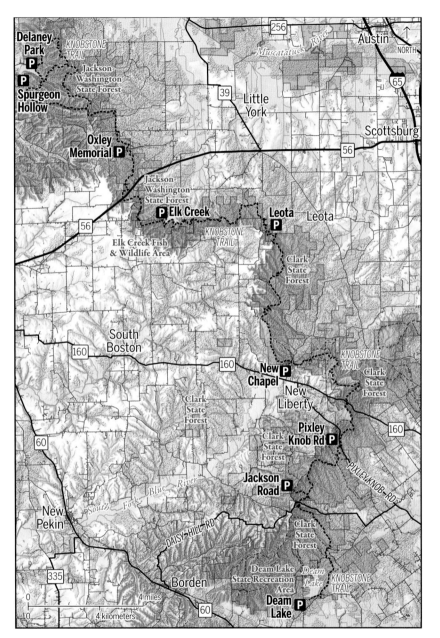

33 KNOBSTONE ESCARPMENT
A Rocky Backbone
38.5161, -85.8707

The Knobstone Escarpment is the most striking physiographic feature in Indiana. Rising 300 to 600 feet above low-lying farmlands, this sinuous ridge forms a rocky backbone through the southeastern part of the state. The prominent landform marks the easternmost extent of the Norman Upland, and its high stone knobs and bluffs form the most rugged topography in the entire state.

From a distance, the escarpment appears as a long unbroken cliff that looms high above the Scottsburg Lowland. The dramatic shift in topography is the result of the differential erosion of rocks of the Mississippian-age Borden Group. To the west, fine-grained sandstone and siltstone of the Edwardsville and Spickert Knob Formations make up the Norman Upland, while to the east the Scottsburg Lowland is formed on New Providence Shale and New Albany Shale. The coarser-grained highlands are more resistant to weathering than the older, softer shale. At the boundary between the two regions, the escarpment forms a high, narrow ridge with distinctive, steeply sided, knobby hills for which it is named.

The Knobstone Escarpment begins in Kentucky and crosses into Indiana in southeast Harrison County. It parallels the Ohio River until New Albany, where it turns northward toward southern Clark County. This 45-mile stretch north of New Albany is the region of greatest relief along the escarpment; the rocky crest rises 400 to 600 feet above valleys to the east, and peaks on the crest reach more than 1,000 feet above sea level. Near Henryville, the Knobstone Escarpment turns sharply northwestward and intersects the East Fork of the White River south of Medora. North of the river, the escarpment is dissected by broad,

Flat-topped ridges and deep V-shaped valleys are typical of the knobby slope between the Norman Upland and Scottsburg Lowland. —Courtesy of Steven Higgs, Natural Bloomington

flat valleys between rounded knobs. The surface exposure of the Knobstone Escarpment ends in southern Johnson County, where sediments from the Wisconsin Stage of glaciation cover it. From here, the escarpment continues northwest under thick drift for another 100 miles to a point southwest of Lafayette.

You can best see the Knobstone Escarpment along the Knobstone Trail. The 58-mile-long backcountry trail is Indiana's longest footpath, and it follows narrow flat-topped ridges through Scott, Washington, and Clark Counties. This popular trail is rugged and difficult and has many steep climbs and descents. For those up to the challenge, the knobby peaks offer scenic views unlike anywhere else in Indiana. One of the best overlooks on the trail is Round Knob where, on a clear day, you can catch glimpses of the Louisville skyline and Ohio River.

34 TUNNEL MILL
Passageway through Fossiliferous Shale
38.9754, -85.6077

Among the rolling hills and winding streams of Jennings County lies a historic stone passageway known as Tunnel Mill. Located south of Vernon in the Crosley Fish and Wildlife Area, Tunnel Mill is the site of a former gristmill on the Muscatatuck River. Unlike Portland Arch and other natural bridges in Indiana, this fossiliferous archway was excavated in the early nineteenth century and today forms a unique exposure of Silurian-age strata in the state.

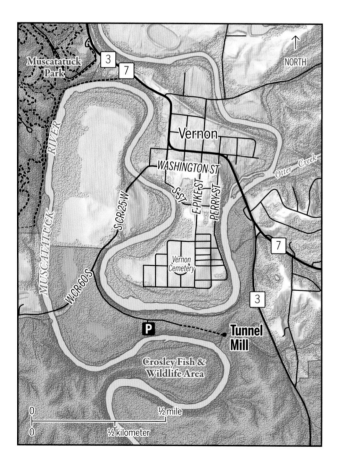

The Muscatatuck River, a scenic waterway whose name means "land of winding rivers" in a Native American language, flows southeast toward the East Fork of the White River. At Vernon, the Muscatatuck River makes a large, entrenched loop, leaving only a narrow ridge between two meanders of the river. Middle Silurian rocks are exposed on both sides of this ridge. The lowest strata belong to the Laurel Member of the Salamonie Dolomite, a light-gray dolomitic limestone that forms the base of the tunnel and extends to the streambed and lower stone ledges. Above the Laurel lies about 3 feet of the Waldron Shale. This soft, blue-gray calcareous shale is famous for its abundant and diverse fossils of crinoids, brachiopods, and gastropods, and it can be traced throughout the central and eastern United States. The hard gray roof of the tunnel is composed of the Louisville Limestone, and the brown layers at the top of the hill are made of the Geneva Dolomite Member of the Jeffersonville Limestone, deposited in Devonian time over an eroded surface on the Silurian rocks.

The Silurian strata here remained as an unbreached berm between two meanders of the Muscatatuck River until 1824, when Ebenezer Baldwin blasted through the soft layers of the Waldron Shale to create Tunnel Mill. The difference in elevation between the north and south entrances of the tunnel provided waterpower, and a 4-foot-wide channel in the center of the tunnel siphoned water toward a gristmill. To visit Tunnel Mill, head south from Vernon on County Road 25 W and turn left onto the hidden turnoff; if you cross the Muscatatuck River, you have gone too far. Drive to the end of the road, park next to Baldwin Cemetery, and walk 0.2 mile down a gravel path within the Crosley Fish and Wildlife Area. You will begin to see glimpses of the tunnel through the trees on your right. Carefully climb down the limestone ledges to explore the excavated channel and mill ruins. Only view the tunnel from the outside because freeze-thaw cycles often cause blocks of stone to collapse inside.

A channel, or millrace, was cut into the underlying Laurel Member to provide increased waterpower for the gristmill.

Fossils readily weather out of the soft blue-gray Waldron Shale along the walls of Tunnel Mill.

83

Remnants of a four-story gristmill still stand on the western shore of the Muscatatuck River. Originally used for grain and flour production, the mill was converted into a paper mill after the Civil War.

35 MUSCATATUCK COUNTY PARK
Vuggy Dolostone Bluffs above a River
38.9885, -85.6184

High bluffs cut by sinuous streams attract climbers and geology enthusiasts alike to Muscatatuck County Park, located 1.5 miles northwest of Tunnel Mill in North Vernon. The park's topography is unique to the Muscatatuck Plateau due to the glacial erosion of Devonian-age strata. Rushing water from the Illinoian and Wisconsin Stages of glaciation carved the fossiliferous rock into an elaborate labyrinth of rugged hills and valleys, with massive cliffs reaching 80 feet above the Muscatatuck River.

The lower bluffs are composed of the Geneva Member of the Jeffersonville Limestone, a vuggy, dark-brown dolomite that forms an erosion-resistant wall along the west bank of the river. Layers in the rock are pockmarked with vugs, small cavities that form from the erosion or dissolution of fossils or mineral crystals. Above the Geneva Member lies light-gray to bluish-gray strata of the Jeffersonville and North Vernon Limestones. Fossils are abundant in the limestone layers, and you can easily spot impressions of brachiopods, colonial corals, and cephalopods in fallen slabs along the streambed. The carbonate bluffs also contain several caves, whose spring-fed openings produce seasonal waterfalls in many of the ravines adjacent to the river channel.

The county park is situated halfway between Vernon and North Vernon on IN 3/IN 7. Turn onto the park road by the stone office building and follow it down to Vinegar Mill, a

historical quarry and stone-cutting mill that operated from 1830 to 1875. Park in the small lot next to the reconstructed mill and take the stairs down to the Geneva Dolomite bluffs along the river. Nicknamed Heinousness Wall, it is a favorite of local rock climbers. Continue upstream on the River Trail to scramble under the limestone bluffs. A few short connector trails dip into rocky ravines between the steep hills and uplands, and the Blue Trail climbs to the top of the bluffs for views of the river valley.

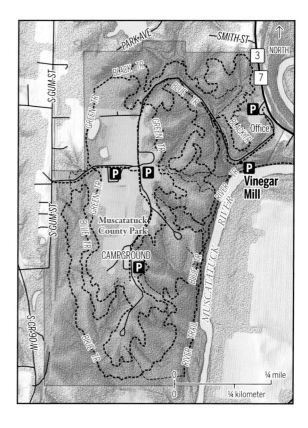

This area was designated Vinegar Mill State Park in 1922 and renamed Muscatatuck State Park in 1923. In 1968, the state gave the property back to Jennings County to create the scenic county park enjoyed today.

The tall, rugged bluffs of Geneva Dolomite are a popular climbing and bouldering spot for adventurous visitors.

Over 10 miles of hiking and biking trails wind along spring-filled ravines on the western edge of the Muscatatuck River.

36 VERSAILLES STATE PARK
Entrenched Stream at a Stratigraphic Boundary
39.0613, -85.2340

Versailles State Park, Indiana's second-largest state park, includes more than 6,000 acres on the eastern edge of the Muscatatuck Plateau. Located less than 2 miles east of downtown Versailles in Ripley County, the park is characterized by meandering streams, forested uplands, and rugged bluffs of Ordovician and Silurian limestone. More than 6 miles of trails follow the wide gorge of Laughery Creek, perfect for tranquil strolls across the fossiliferous bedrock.

Park exposures of southwestward-dipping limestone and shale belong to the Whitewater and Dillsboro Formations. These rocks preserve an influx of marine life that immigrated to southeastern Indiana when the sea level rose at the end of the Ordovician Period. The rocky hills and streambeds exposed here are significantly older than those at nearby Tunnel Mill and Muscatatuck County Park, owing to the regional dip of the bedrock. Laughery Creek straddles the stratigraphic boundary between the Ordovician and Silurian rocks, so only the bluffs west of the creek are mantled by a thin layer of Silurian rock.

The wide valley and deep ravines along Laughery Creek first formed during the Pleistocene Epoch. Ice sheets from the Illinoian Stage of glaciation extended into southeastern Indiana 300,000 to 132,000 years ago, depositing a thick cover of till over the ancient bedrock. When the ice retreated, meltwater rushed south toward the newly formed Ohio River and quickly eroded the glacial sediments and soft bedrock. The mighty meltwater battered the alternating layers of calcareous shale and rubbly limestone, and Laughery Creek became entrenched, or trapped, in its deepening channel.

Brachiopods Platystrophia *and* Rafinesquina *are the most commonly exposed fossils in the Ordovician strata along Laughery Creek and its tributaries.*

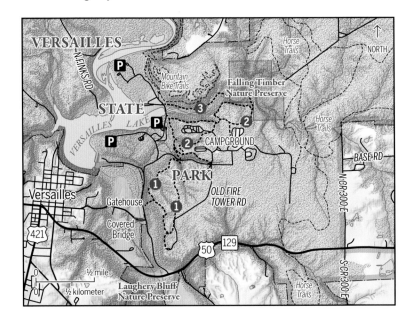

Fallen Timber Creek flows through a deeply entrenched valley with 100-foot-high bluffs. —Courtesy of Steven Higgs, Natural Bloomington

The best way to experience the timeworn topography is to hike along one of the park's three trails. You can follow Trail 1 along a moderate 2.25-mile-long loop to see sinkholes in the limestone and scenic ravines in an old-growth forest. For more of a challenge, take the connector trail up from Versailles Lake to Trail 2. Trails 2 and 3 skirt the edges of Fallen Timber Creek and feature rocky slopes with seasonal waterfalls. Exposed rock layers in this area are full of fossils, but please remember that collecting is prohibited on park property.

The historic Busching Bridge crosses Laughery Creek near the park entrance.

37 CLIFTY FALLS STATE PARK
Waterfalls, Canyons, and the Birth of a River
38.7422, -85.4127

Clifty Falls is a picturesque state park located 2 miles west of the historic town of Madison. Situated on the northern bank of the Ohio River, it boasts five 60-foot or higher waterfalls, sheer rocky cliffs, and hiking trails that wind through a rugged, 3-mile-long canyon. The park's steep carbonate bluffs are home to some of the oldest rock exposures in the state and form an ancient drainage divide that helped determine the shape of Indiana.

The park property encompasses 1,519 acres along the eastern edge of Clifty Canyon, a long and narrow gully whose walls have been carved out of bedrock. The lowest slopes of Clifty Canyon formed from Early Ordovician rocks. The Dillsboro Formation occurs in the bottom 270 feet of the canyon, and its soft, limey shale layers erode easily to form the undercuts of the park's waterfalls. The middle layer of the canyon (35 to 40 feet) is the Saluda Member of the Whitewater Formation, whose thick carbonate beds make up the resistant lip of each of the high waterfalls. Silurian-age strata is exposed above the falls in the uppermost 60 to 65 feet of the canyon.

While the rocks that compose the rugged, cliff-lined gorge are 444 to 359 million years old, the scenic topography enjoyed today formed much more recently. Prior to the Pleistocene Epoch, a major drainage divide existed here, separating the Kentucky and Teays Rivers to the east and the ancestral Ohio River to the west. The course of the modern Ohio River did not yet exist, and local streams flowed to the northwest. Beginning 300,000 years ago, ice sheets of the Illinoian Stage of glaciation advanced to the present-day park and blocked these drainage routes, forcing streams to reverse their flow and cut across the Madison divide, giving birth to the modern Ohio River. Torrents of glacial meltwater carved a deep, wide valley along the new Ohio River, and Big Clifty Creek and its tributaries began to weather the soft Ordovician shales to form the canyon and waterfalls. Today, Clifty Canyon grows a quarter-inch each year as the waterfalls continue to erode upstream.

You can explore each of the park's cascading waterfalls by hiking Trails 2, 4, 5, and 7 along Clifty Canyon. Trails here range from moderate to very rugged but offer scenic views within the Muscatatuck Plateau. After visiting Little Clifty Falls, cross the bridge and follow a short loop to a wedge-shaped boulder

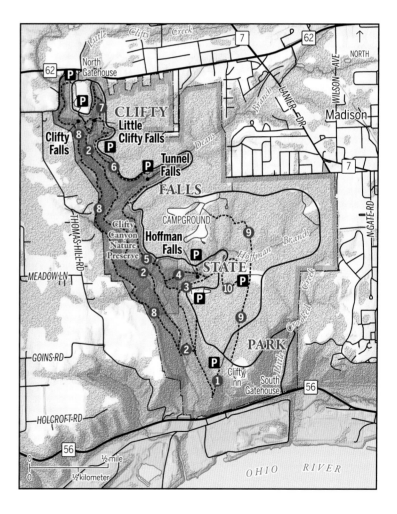

All five of the main waterfalls, including Big Clifty Falls shown here, formed near the surface, or contact, between the Saluda Member of the Whitewater Formation and the underlying Dillsboro Formation.

Water from Deans Branch cascades over an icy ledge before entering Clifty Canyon 83 feet below. Tunnel Falls is the tallest waterfall in the park. —Courtesy of Henry H. Gray

called Cake Rock, a remnant of the Saluda Member that was undercut by the erosive power of Little Clifty Creek. Waterfalls flow year-round, and can range from delicate bridal veils to gushing torrents, depending on the weather. For sweeping views of the Ohio River and historic Madison, climb to the top of the Observation Tower on Trail 1. A bedrock ridge known as Devil's Backbone lies in the distance of this panorama, formed when ice diverted a former channel of the Ohio River to its present-day valley. Fossils are plentiful in the rocky overhangs, but please take only photographs as collecting is not permitted on state property.

Cake Rock is located on Trail 7 near Little Clifty Falls.

Water stairsteps down thin limestone ledges before plunging 72 feet at Hoffman Falls.
—Courtesy of Lee Mandrell, Leman's Studios

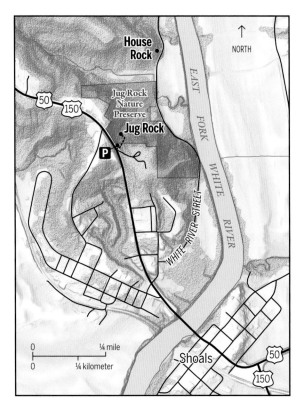

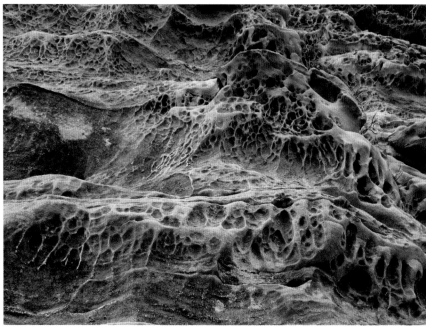

Sand grains erode from the surface of the sandstone to produce a unique pitted texture called honeycomb weathering.

38 JUG ROCK NATURE PRESERVE
Freestanding Sandstone Pillar
38.6762, -86.7966

Located just off US 50 at Shoals is one of Indiana's most peculiar geological formations. Jug Rock is a rare, freestanding tea table rock named for its curious resemblance to an old-fashioned water pitcher. About 60 feet high and 20 feet wide, this column of Pennsylvanian-age sandstone rises above the forested valley of the East Fork of the White River with no support from adjacent ledges. It is the largest table rock east of the Mississippi River.

Jug Rock is primarily composed of cross-bedded quartz sandstone from the Mansfield Formation. The flat, projecting layer at the top (known locally as the "stopper") appears to balance precariously on the cylindrical base. The bulge of the jug features inclined cross-beds and a pitted, honeycomb-like texture, and the base is composed of thickly bedded sandstone with quartz pebbles. Iron deposited by circulating groundwater has oxidized on the surface of the sandstone to produce its reddish color and, incidentally, to harden the outcrop face.

Over time, the erosional power of frost, plant roots, and running water created Jug Rock's distinct shape. Prior to becoming an isolated pillar, Jug Rock was an angular block of

The fluted column of Jug Rock is made of cross-bedded sandstone of the Pennsylvanian-age Mansfield Formation.

sandstone attached to the nearby ridge. Natural fractures, or joints, in the bedrock allowed water to erode downward, removing layers of less-resistant shale, conglomerate, and thin sandstone along the joint planes. As these fractures widened, erosion smoothed the isolated sandstone block. Across the valley to the northeast is House Rock, an eroded alcove created by massive blocks of sandstone with a similar widening fracture pattern.

To access Jug Rock Nature Preserve, park in the small gravel lot directly off US 50 (not on Albright Lane) and walk down the footpath to the rock formation below. House Rock is a short drive away on White River Street.

39 HINDOSTAN FALLS
Glacial Grooves in Flat Rock
38.6245, -86.8512

A very unusual meander cutoff occurs about 5 miles southwest of Shoals near Hindostan Falls. Nestled in the hilly terrain of the Crawford Upland, the East Fork of the White River widens and ripples over a wide sandstone ledge. The abandoned meander and subsequent waterfall that you see today formed in the Early Pleistocene Epoch. Prior to the development of the meander cutoff, the White River turned north upstream of the falls before winding southward toward Dubois County. As glacial ice covered the region, subglacial meltwater streams carved linear grooves into the underlying sandstone bedrock. These 3-to-8-inch-wide grooves are visible in Flat Rock, the flat-topped slab of Mansfield Formation sandstone exposed downstream from the present-day falls. Over time, the entrenched meander valley filled with glacial sediments and collapsed, shortening the course of the river by nearly 5 miles. The shift in the river's course allowed water to break over the eastern edge of Flat Rock, and continued erosion upstream established Hindostan Falls where it is today.

Although of interest because of its geology, Hindostan Falls is actually best known for its history. A town here, founded in 1816, grew rapidly, and many mills, homes, and whetstone factories dotted the riverbanks. By 1820, the population of Hindostan Falls had reached 1,200, similar in size at the time to Louisville, Kentucky, making it one of the largest settlements in Indiana. In 1822, townsfolk were struck with a "terrible sickness" (likely cholera), and the town was abandoned. A look at Flat Rock reveals square holes among the glacially carved channels. These curious holes were cut for the placement of a timber-framed dam and today provide one of the only physical traces of the town.

Streams flowing underneath glacial ice eroded 2-to-4-inch-deep channels into the sandstone bedrock. Bedding planes in the sandstone cross the eastward-oriented grooves at oblique angles.

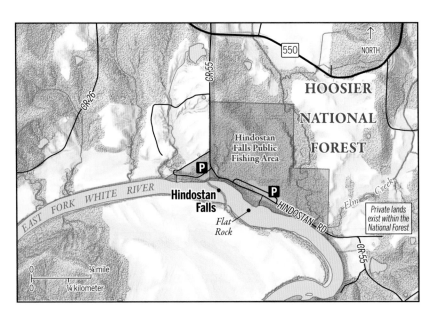

Whitewater breaks over the 4-to-6-foot-high sandstone ledge at Hindostan Falls, one of the largest waterfalls by volume in Indiana.

Aerial view of Flat Rock exposed at low water levels. The flat, grassy area to the left of the falls and Flat Rock is the abandoned meander of the East Fork of the White River.
—Courtesy of Henry H. Gray

CROWN HILL CEMETERY
History in Hindostan Whetstone
38.6032, -86.1073

A short stroll around any graveyard will reveal that some head-stones' fading epitaphs do not last long into the hereafter. From locally produced limestone and sandstone to granite and marble from faraway quarries, the variety of native and imported stones in cemeteries can provide historical geology buffs with the perfect opportunity to examine weathering rates on different rock types over easily measurable periods of time. One of the best places to begin such a study is Crown Hill Cemetery, located a half mile from the Washington County Courthouse in Salem. A particular type of grave marker at Crown Hill exemplifies the erosion-resistant properties of a unique Hoosier stone.

The best-preserved grave markers are made from a tan, thinly laminated Mississippian-age siltstone known as Hind-ostan Whetstone. Found in more than 250 cemeteries in 30 counties in Indiana, the markers were exclusively quarried and manufactured within a small region of northwestern Orange County during the early to mid-nineteenth century. Fashioned from the scraps of popular sharpening stones, the whetstone's millimeter-scale layering and uniform quartz grain size made it the perfect medium for carvers, who split and chiseled tablet-like slabs into a variety of shapes. When the New Albany & Salem Railroad (the Monon) was completed in the 1850s, grave markers made of other types of stone were introduced, and whetstone quickly lost favor. Today, the silica-rich whetstone grave markers appear essentially untouched more than 150 years later, while some limestone and many older marble headstones can be very difficult to read because rainwater, which is slightly acidic, has dissolved the carbonate rock.

A unique characteristic of Hindostan Whetstone is its pervasive, repetitive pattern of thick and thin laminae (layers), resembling a deck of cards, along the edges of the grave markers. Composed of sediments deposited 300 million years ago in an ancient tidal flat, the thicker layers of silt were deposited as tides rose, while the thinner layers were laid down at low tide. These alternating couplets are known as tidal rhythmites and represent one complete rotation of the Moon around its axis (a lunar day). The thickness of each individual couplet directly equates to daily or semidaily changes in tidal current and height, making it possible to determine the lunar phase during the time of deposition. Tidal rhythmites are unequivocal evidence of marine conditions in a sedimentary basin, and the Hindostan Whetstone is known internationally because of its geologic and astronomical importance. To see these remarkable deposits for yourself, take IN 56/IN 60 to Salem and follow South Harrison Street to the cemetery entrance. Rows of historic whetstone grave markers are in the northeastern part of the cemetery, where elaborate carvings stand out in stunning detail and you can count the time-frozen tides along the edge of each headstone.

Established in 1824, Crown Hill Cemetery is home to the largest concentration of Hindostan Whetstone grave markers in Indiana.
—Photo courtesy of Richard L. Powell

The wider laminae were deposited during high tides and the very thin laminae during low tides. Each couplet denotes a day of deposition.
—Photo courtesy of Richard L. Powell

The still-sharp carving on this grave marker illustrates how the silica-rich Hindostan Whetstone resists weathering. —Photo courtesy of Richard L. Powell

41 SPRING MILL STATE PARK
Cavernous Conduits under a Pioneer Village
38.7233, -86.4170

The reasons why people settled where they did often can be traced directly to an area's geology. Few places in Indiana display this cultural connection to landscape better than Spring Mill. The abundant waterpower from the cavern system made it possible for Spring Mill to become a bustling nineteenth-century town. Located 3 miles east of Mitchell off IN 60, Spring Mill was established as a pioneer community in 1815. The springs that flow from cave entrances were a consistent source of water for early settlers, who quickly built several gristmills, a wool mill, a sawmill, and a distillery. In 1817, a

water-powered gristmill was constructed of 3-foot-thick blocks of locally quarried St. Louis Limestone. Water from Hamer Cave flows north into a trellised flume, splashing over the mill's large water wheel to turn grindstones to make flour. Today, the gristmill is the centerpiece of the restored pioneer village at Spring Mill State Park.

The park's landscape is a classic example of the sinkholes, sinking streams, caves, and springs that make up the Mitchell Plateau. Situated in an area of relatively low relief between the Crawford and Norman Uplands, the Mitchell Plateau formed on

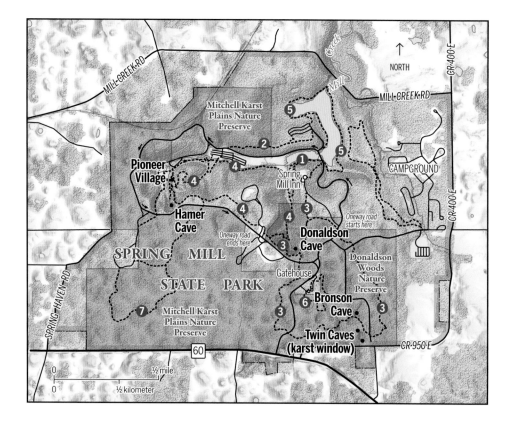

a thick sequence of Mississippian-age carbonate rocks that has been intensely influenced by karst development. Precipitation passes through joints in the bedrock, dissolving the rock to form sinkholes that feed water into subterranean passageways. The area southwest of the park is the defining locality of the Mitchell Plateau and one of the best examples of karst topography in the world.

Several caves dot the park grounds, with the large cavernous conduits mostly within the upper Salem Limestone. Underground streams follow parallel passages that connect with right-angle bends due to the long, linear joints that occur perpendicular to one another in the bedrock. A short hike up from the Pioneer Village leads to the entrance of Hamer Cave, which discharges groundwater that has traveled from as far west as IN 37.

The trellised flume diverts water from Mill Creek to the gristmill at Pioneer Village.

To the southeast lies the entrance to Twin Caves, a favorite for geologists and visitors alike. Mapped at a length of 9,134 feet, Twin Caves is accessible through a specific feature known as a karst window, which forms from the collapse of a cavern roof. Subsurface water from Upper Twin Cave emerges briefly before disappearing into Lower Twin Cave. Visitors can follow stairs through the area where the cave roof used to be to the boat dock at Upper Twin Cave; a boat tour is available in the summer months. Experienced cavers can also explore Donaldson Cave, Bronson Cave, Upper Twin Cave, and the Cave River Valley Natural Area with authorization from the Indiana Department of Natural Resources.

Water from the Mosquito Creek swallow hole flows through the underground passages of Twin Caves before exiting the Donaldson Cave entrance.

42 LOST RIVER
Disappearing Stream in Karst Topography
38.6100, -86.4579

The Lost River drainage basin is one of the best-known karst areas in the United States. Beginning in western Washington County, the 90-mile-long disappearing stream transects Orange County through the sinkhole-dotted terrain of the Mitchell Plateau. As its name implies, most of the river is "lost" to sinks and swallow holes that divert surface water into an underground cave system that flows beneath surficial drainage divides.

The complex drainage relationships along the Lost River karst area can be divided into three distinct parts. The 7.5-mile eastern segment is a normal surface-flowing stream. As it flows southwest toward IN 37, the stream valley narrows and begins to drop into Mississippian-age bedrock. Here in the central segment, the thick clay deposits that covered the bedrock in the eastern section have been stripped away, allowing slightly acidic water to percolate through the carbonate rock and form sinkholes, caves, and subterranean tunnels. The Lost River enters the first sink 2.7 miles southeast of Orleans, leaving a 22-mile dry channel downstream. During spring runoff and times of extreme rainfall, water flows down the dry bed from sink to sink; when a conduit fills, surface water flows down to the next swallow hole. The sinkhole plain captures almost all surficial water in this area, with as many as 1,022 sinks in a square mile.

As the dry bed of the Lost River meanders through the rolling karst landscape, underground waters travel west through more than 20 miles of complex passageways before emerging as a large spring at the Orangeville Rise. The final western segment of the Lost River begins at that large spring, which is discussed in the next site description. Downstream of the True Rise of the Lost River, where more groundwater emerges at the surface, the river returns to normal surface flow and travels through a deeply entrenched valley before reaching the East Fork of the White River. Altogether, the Lost River and its tributaries drain about 366 square miles in the river's impressive 90-mile trek through this distinctive terrain.

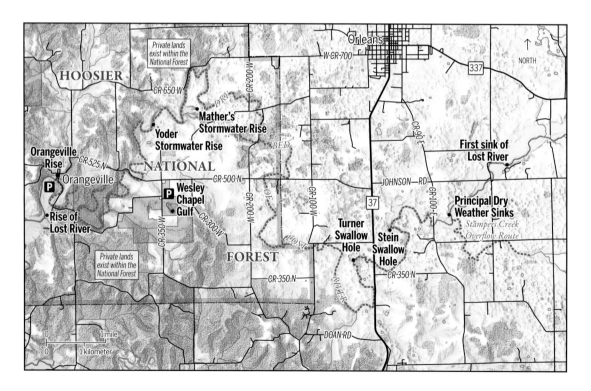

Known as sinks or swallows, the sinkhole depressions along the central segment of the Lost River divert surficial water underground, creating an entirely dry streambed.

Aerial photo of a dense sinkhole field in the Mitchell Plateau.
—Courtesy of Sam Frushour

43 WESLEY CHAPEL GULF AND ORANGEVILLE RISE

Subterranean Windows

38.6231, -86.5224 and 38.6311, -86.5571

About 2.5 miles east of Orangeville within the Hoosier National Forest, a unique collapse sinkhole known as the Wesley Chapel Gulf leads into the winding subterranean passageways of the Lost River Cave System. Formed by the collapse of an underground cave network, this deep cove (or gulf) is 1,075 feet long, about 350 feet wide, and surrounded by 25-to-95-foot-high limestone cliffs that obscure the surrounding countryside. In the center of the sunken basin lies a 14-foot-deep pool of bright blue-green water. A cave stream running west from the subterranean Lost River rises some 35 feet into the southeastern rim of the gulf before following a series of sinks and disappearing at a major swallow hole underneath a cliff of Mississippian-age Ste. Genevieve Limestone. Downed logs and scattered timber around the gulf reflect the occasional flooding that occurs here, which can cover the floor of the gulf with water several feet deep.

A short drive to the west will take you to the Orangeville Rise, the second largest spring in Indiana and the next ascent of the subterranean Lost River. Here, the disappearing stream rises 30 feet through bedrock conduits and emerges at the base of a rocky alcove. Underneath the limestone ledge, spring openings rapidly discharge 9 to 180 cubic feet of water per second into a green pool. Downstream at the True Rise of the Lost River, groundwater travels through a vertical 160-foot slotlike channel to meet the Lost River at the surface for the river's final journey. Because of these impressive geologic features, Wesley Chapel Gulf and the Orangeville Rise are designated as National Natural Landmarks and are protected by the Indiana Karst Conservancy, Nature Conservancy, and US Forest Service.

Wesley Chapel Gulf is one of the largest collapse sinkholes in Indiana and is much larger than most karst windows.

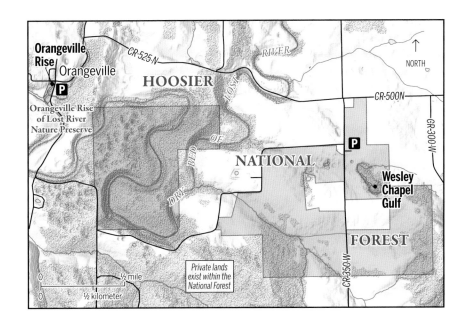

Water at the Orangeville Rise is collected from 41 square miles of sinkholes and sinking streams located to the northeast, near Mitchell and northwest of Orangeville.

WEBER LAKE
Coal Mine Reclamation
38.1095, -87.0109

In a state park dedicated to the boyhood home of our six-teenth president, a small, rectangular-shaped lake preserves a crucial connection to Indiana's mining history. Located in the northwestern corner of Lincoln State Park in Spencer County, Weber Lake is the site of a coal mine reclamation project that restored a highly acidic "dead lake." It is an exemplary success story in the treatment of acid mine drainage.

The origins of Indiana's coal resources began 318 to 299 million years ago, when the eastern and central United States was located near the equator and covered by a tropical swamp forest. As trees, ferns, and jointed stem rushes grew and died, plant debris accumulated in thick layers of organic-rich peat on the swamp floor. Buried by subsequent deposits of sediment that became rock, the peat was chemically altered by heat and pressure to form coal. These coal deposits are part of the Pennsylvanian-age Raccoon Creek and Carbondale Groups and are mined exclusively in the southwestern part of the state.

From 1950 to 1958, a 3-foot-thick seam of the Minshall/Buffaloville Coal Member was surface mined at the area now called Weber Lake. Unlike underground mining, where coal is extracted by tunneling underground, this coal was mined by stripping away unwanted rock and soil (overburden) from the Earth's surface. As the pit grew wider, a steep berm (highwall) was created and piles of overburden were discarded around the excavated area. Railroad lines transported the coal to a weigh station, located along the park's Trail 4, before the coal trains traveled south to the Ohio River. When the mine was abandoned in 1958, the 19-acre pit filled with water to form Weber Lake.

As groundwater and precipitation filtered through the piles of debris, or spoil piles, to the lake, sulfur-bearing materials in the coal waste reacted with oxygen and water to produce highly acidic water. This runoff, known as acid mine drainage, created an environment too toxic for fish, insects, or plants to survive, and Weber Lake was declared "dead." In 2001,

the Abandoned Mine Lands Reclamation Project began work to restore the waterway. Through chemical and passive treat-ments, scientists neutralized the highly acidic water, stabilized the highwall, and built a levee and seasonal wetland on the east side of the lake. Acting as a natural sponge, species of sedges, cattails, and other wetland plants filter the water, removing acidic material before it enters the lake, and also prevent flooding and recharge groundwater. Today, these reclamation efforts have created a beautiful, thriving habitat for fish, frogs, and migratory birds. To see the changes for yourself, follow the easy 1.8-mile interpretive loop on Trail 6 around the lake.

About a 30-foot thickness of organic-rich peat was required to form the 3-foot-thick seam of coal that was mined at Weber Lake in the 1950s.

The seasonal wetland in the foreground of this photograph filters water that flows through spoil piles before it reaches the lake.

45 ANGEL MOUNDS STATE HISTORIC SITE
A Mississippian Mystery
37.9477, -87.4492

Along the expansive riverbanks of the Ohio River lies a prehistoric metropolis known as Angel Mounds. Located about 8 miles southeast of Evansville in the lower Ohio River Valley, Angel Mounds was an important settlement of the Mississippian culture. The Native American earthwork structures at Angel Mounds reveal clues to the prehistoric and seismic activity that occurred in southwestern Indiana from AD 1050 to 1450. The historic site includes an interpretive center, re-creations of Mississippian buildings, and a nature preserve with hiking and biking trails.

The Mississippian culture was a mound-building civilization that stretched across North America from AD 800 until 1600. At the core of this culture were the Middle Mississippians, a complex group of people who resided in the central Mississippi River Valley, lower Ohio River Valley, and Upper South. Inhabitants of this region were skilled craftspeople who produced distinctive pottery, stone tools, and jewelry, and practiced intensive corn agriculture. Their settlements were often permanent communities encircled by a wall or palisade.

Second in size only to Cahokia Mounds in Illinois, Angel Mounds was once a thriving village of up to 1,000 people until its abandonment sometime around AD 1450. The 100-acre community featured many grass-thatch houses, an external palisade wall, a central plaza, and eleven earthen mounds. The two largest mounds (A and F) were constructed in stages from AD 1050 to AD 1400. Data from solid earth cores and geophysical profiles revealed the complex history hidden in these platform-shaped structures; the upper platform of Mound A was built rapidly, while its lower platform was expanded at least twice, and Mound F was constructed in three separate phases around AD 1050, AD 1200, and AD 1400. One large question lingers to those who walk among the deserted ruins: Why did they leave? Was the soil depleted,

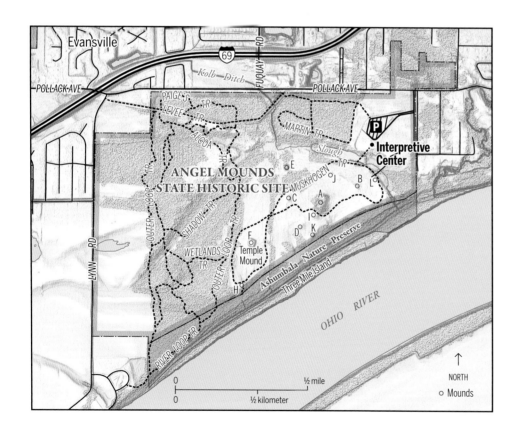

Measuring 42 feet at its highest point, Mound A stands over a large open plaza that was used as a Mississippian community space.

causing the food supply to dwindle? Did environmental changes lead to unpredictable crop harvests? Was there political conflict? Perhaps the answer lies in the geology.

Angel Mounds is located within the Wabash Valley Seismic Zone, an area of concentrated faults that occurs between Vincennes and Evansville. Moderately damaging earthquakes happen in this region every 10 to 20 years, and small earthquakes are felt one or two times a year. Larger earthquakes are known to have occurred in the past 25,000 years. Liquefaction features have been documented along the Wabash and Ohio Rivers in southern Indiana. Formed by large earthquakes with magnitudes greater than 5.5, pressurized mixtures of sand and water were forced upward through fractures in the soil to form irregular dikes of sand known as sand blows. Two such sand bodies occur in Mound F. Different from the surrounding mound fill, these sand blows are related to a significant earthquake that occurred sometime after AD 1100. While intense seismic activity could have affected mound construction and persuaded the Mississippians to leave, the reason for their abrupt abandonment remains a mystery lost to time.

Aerial view of a platform-shaped mound near the Ohio River. —Courtesy of Mike Linderman

46 NEW HARMONY
Birthplace of American Geology
38.1283, -87.9363

On the banks of the Wabash River, New Harmony is the site of two nineteenth-century social experiments. The town was first settled in 1814 by the Harmonists, a religious sect founded by George Rapp. They brought order and community to the Indiana wilderness. Eleven years later, "that wonder of the west" was purchased by Robert Owen and William Maclure, social and scientific reformers who sought to create an educational and communal utopia. Here some of the greatest minds in the natural sciences and educational reform advanced the knowledge that contributed to the formation of the US Geological Survey, Smithsonian Institute, Indiana Geological Survey, and several other midwestern geological surveys.

Owen and Maclure began their secular communal experiment in 1825. Gathering in Philadelphia, a group of about 40 scientists, artists, and educators set out to form a "New Moral World" on the Indiana frontier. Christened the "Boatload of Knowledge," these travelers sailed from Pittsburgh, down the Ohio River and up the Wabash River, to New Harmony. Maclure began the community's educational programs and, upon Owen's departure in 1827, developed New Harmony

The weathervane on the roof of the Owen lab depicts a blastoid, an Archimedes bryozoan, and fossil fish. The corkscrew-like Archimedes was first named and described by David Dale Owen.

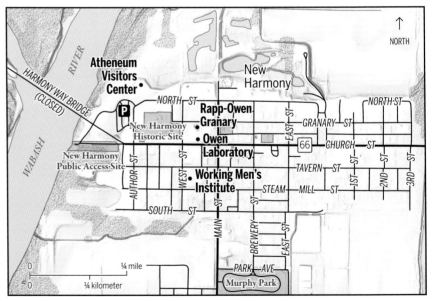

The 3-foot-thick stone walls of the Rapp-Owen Granary are made of locally quarried Pennsylvanian-age sandstone of the Bond Formation.

into a progressive center for scientific advancement. Known as the "father of American geology," Maclure attracted pioneering naturalists from every corner of the globe. Charles Alexandre Lesueur, Thomas Say, Gerard Troost, and Charles Lyell are among the famous scientists who gathered at New Harmony. David Dale Owen and Richard Owen, two of Robert Owen's sons, went on to become the first and third state geologists of Indiana.

Today, this hub of scientific advancement is preserved as a state historic site. Near its center lies the Working Men's Institute. A legacy of Maclure's philanthropic efforts, the Working Men's Institute is one of 114 such libraries that Maclure gifted to Indiana and Illinois upon his death. The first floor holds Indiana's oldest continuously operating library, and the second floor contains a museum with fossil and mineral specimens collected during Maclure's time. Two geological laboratories still stand. The Rapp-Owen Granary, a four-story brick and stone building at the corner of Granary and West Streets, was home to the first federally appointed geological survey (1837 to 1856). Directly to the south, the Owen Laboratory housed geologic specimens collected by David Dale Owen, Indiana's first state geologist. The laboratory's geological-themed weathervane is visible through the surrounding gardens. You can tour the exterior of this and other historic buildings in town—a must-see for anyone interested in the history of geology.

47 WYANDOTTE CAVES
Breakdown Mountains inside Dry Caverns
38.2291, -86.2936

About 4 miles northeast of Leavenworth in O'Bannon Woods State Park, a series of dry passageways and large collapse features lie beneath the eastern edge of the Crawford Upland. More than 9 miles of subterranean tunnels wind through Mississippian bedrock and include three separate caverns—Wyandotte Cave, Little Wyandotte Cave, and Easter Pit Cave. The storied passages have welcomed explorers for over 4,000 years, and massive underground amphitheaters and stunning cave formations make this a key stop for anyone interested in Indiana's cavernous spaces.

The uppermost passages at Wyandotte Caves began to form 2.6 to 1 million years ago after a series of tectonic uplifts caused streams to erode valleys into the carbonate bedrock. As slightly acidic water infiltrated joints and fractures in the limestone, it dissolved the rock and created larger openings. An underground drainage system formed, allowing more water to dissolve the almost parallel passageways at multiple depths. Over time, the streams eroded below the level of the nearby Blue River, and Wyandotte's lengthy halls were left high and dry.

One of the most fascinating features of Wyandotte Cave is the Pillar of the Constitution, a 35-foot-tall, 70-foot-wide column made of white calcite. —Courtesy of Richard L. Powell

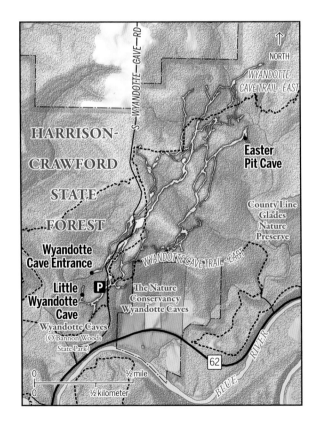

White, fibrous crystals of the magnesium sulfate mineral epsomite were mined from Wyandotte Cave in the early 1800s for medicinal salts. —Courtesy of Samuel S. Frushour

Standing 135 feet tall, Monument Mountain formed from collapsed layers of rock from the cave ceiling and walls. —Courtesy of Richard L. Powell

While the entrance to Wyandotte Cave and other high ceilings are within the Paoli Limestone, the majority of the cave system is formed within the thick, light-colored beds of the Ste. Genevieve Limestone. Many of the passageways are floored with thick sediment, and larger openings are filled with broken ceiling and wall rock, called breakdown. In most of the cave, you can see bands of irregular lenses and nodules of the Lost River Chert Bed protruding from the limestone walls. About 2,000 feet from the entrance, a massive pile of breakdown known as Monument Mountain stands 135 feet tall, forming the largest underground mountain in Indiana. Farther north, the Pillar of the Constitution—the state's largest cave column—towers at 35 feet in height. A narrow passageway in the southern part of the cave system is lined with delicate, gravity-defying spirals at the Garden of Helictites, providing a rare glimpse of one of the most bizarre cave formations.

Beginning 4,000 years ago, Archaic and Woodland Native Americans entered the cave to mine flint (chert), epsomite, and aragonite minerals. European settlers began exploring the cave around 1798. From 1810 through 1817, it was known as Epsom Salt Cave, and the long, fibrous white crystals of epsomite were mined for medicinal salts. In 1850, Wyandotte opened as a show cave. To explore the breathtaking rooms and passages, follow South Wyandotte Cave Road to the state park office. The easy half-hour tour of Little Wyandotte Cave offers extensive views of tapered cave formations, and the more difficult tour of Wyandotte Cave explores large breakdown passageways over a two-hour trek.

48 BLUESPRING CAVERNS
Boat Tour through Underground Angles
38.7961, -86.5458

Elongated pillars of stone hanging from smooth, water-carved walls are just one of the many fascinating cave formations you'll see when you take the river voyage at Bluespring Caverns. Located about 6 miles southwest of Bedford in Lawrence County, Bluespring Caverns is the northernmost show cave in Indiana and home to the longest known subterranean boat tour in the United States. The Myst'ry River and its underground tributaries follow the cave through right-angle passageways under the Mitchell Plateau.

In the Mitchell Plateau and Crawford Upland of south-central Indiana, Mississippian-age bedrock dips 25 feet per mile to the southwest, controlling the direction of underground drainage. Widespread dissolution of limestone occurs along well-defined joints, fractures, and bedding planes as water flows to the southwest. Unburdened by the thick glacial drift that covers much of the state, caves and karst began to form sometime between 2.6 and 1 million years ago, during the Pleistocene Epoch, after a series of tectonic uplifts caused streams to become entrenched in steep valleys. Later in the Pleistocene Epoch, continental-scale glaciers extended into Indiana, and meltwater flowing from them carved the caverns and valleys to deeper and deeper levels.

Bluespring Caverns was discovered in the late 1800s, when early explorers entered the cave through a spring opening near the East Fork of the White River. In 1940, the bottom of a sinkhole pond collapsed overnight, exposing a canyon-like corridor with a flowing underground river. The cave had formed along joints within the Salem Limestone that were widened by precipitation flowing from sinkholes in the overlying St. Louis

Stalactites and soda straws align along fractures in the Salem Limestone ceiling.

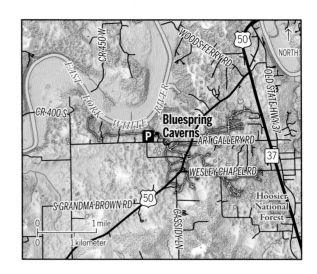

Boat tours follow part of the underground Myst'ry River at Bluespring Caverns. —Courtesy of Sam Frushour

Limestone. The joints occur perpendicular to one another in the bedrock, creating numerous right-angle bends in the cave. Bluespring Caverns has multiple levels of solution-formed passageways, totaling over 20 miles in length. The Myst'ry River flows through a large lower passage, and many of the side conduits have smaller streams with some dry passages at higher levels. About 3 miles of the Myst'ry River are navigable by boat, and water levels are supplied year-round by the extensive network of sinkholes in the surrounding karst region.

To take a guided boat tour through this solution cave, head southwest from Bedford on US 50 to Blue Springs Cavern Road and park at the visitors center before walking down a steep paved path to the vegetation-covered entrance. Look up at the former ceiling of a collapsed sinkhole before heading into the dark, damp atmosphere of the cave, which stays at a constant 53 degrees Fahrenheit. Before boarding the boat at the dock, note the delicate tubes of calcite, called soda straws, clinging to ceiling joints. Boat tours last about one hour and lead upstream past hanging, icicle-like stalactites and broad flowstone deposits. Just before the turnaround, you can set eyes upon the Rock of Gibraltar, a large buttress undercut by the erosive cave stream. Bluespring Caverns is home to several specially adapted animals, such as salamanders, bats, and blind cavefish, and its streams continue to carve new depths below the Hoosier heartland.

49 INDIANA CAVERNS
Indiana's Longest Cave
38.1821, -86.1493

Below the sinkhole-dotted fields of Harrison County, more than 44 miles of limestone passageways entomb ice age mammal bones at Indiana Caverns, part of the seventh-longest cave in the United States and Indiana's longest cave. Located 3 miles southwest of Corydon in the historic Binkley Cave System, Indiana Caverns opened as a show cave in 2012. The

rocky corridors began to form 2.6 to 1 million years ago in the Early Pleistocene Epoch, and water from the Crawford Upland and Mitchell Plateau continues to sink underground to dissolve a maze of pathways before emerging as springs along the Indian and Blue Rivers.

The Binkley Cave System is composed of three levels of passageways connected by intersecting shafts. The long, winding tunnels extend for miles and vary from small crawlways to large rooms. The highest level is located 25 to 30 feet below the ground surface and includes mostly dry mudbanks and a large rock-walled room known as Big Bone Mountain. The ceiling of this uppermost level is composed of thick Ste. Genevieve Limestone, and the rest of the cave is formed in thin beds of St. Louis Limestone. A small opening near the contact of these two Mississippian-age units within Big Bone Mountain was a treacherous doorway for ice age mammals. Lured by the cool, damp air, hoglike peccaries, short-faced bears, and saber-toothed cats entered the small fissure 50,000 to 12,000 years ago and tumbled down piles of fallen ceiling rock to become trapped inside the cave. Indiana Caverns contains a large concentration of peccary bones, and the extensive trackways, hoof marks, and fully articulated skeletons make this cave system a treasure trove for paleontologists. Below the publicly accessible passages, the intermediate and lower levels contain flowing cave streams near the water table, 70 to 200 feet below the surface. Active exploration is ongoing and new passages are discovered each year.

To visit this ice age marvel, take IN 135 south from Corydon and head west on Shiloh Road SW through a well-developed sinkhole plain. The tour

Stalactites and narrow, layered draperies known as cave bacon are located near the entrance to Big Bone Mountain.

The boat tour passes a speleothem known as the Heart of the Cave, nicknamed because of its striking similarity to a human heart. —Courtesy of Lee Mandrell, Leman's Studios

The blue light near the ceiling of Big Bone Mountain illuminates an entrance where ice age peccaries and other large mammals fell to their deaths inside the cave. Paleontologists at the Indiana State Museum study the abundant bones of these animals, and several skeletons are on display at the museum. —Courtesy of Lee Mandrell, Leman's Studios

begins below the visitors center, where a large opening was blasted in 2012 to reveal stunning cave formations. Visitors pass a 40-foot waterfall before entering Big Bone Mountain. Look for dark globular balls of chert and occasional coral fossils protruding from the walls of St. Louis Limestone. Climb the stairs past peccary graveyards to Sleeping Bear Boulevard, where a carnivorous short-faced bear rested between peccary hunts. The boat tour along the Eerie Canal leads you past shallow rimstone pools filled with translucent and blind fish, crayfish, and other arthropods. At the surface, the 0.2-mile Cave Interpretive Trail travels atop the underground tunnels with signs explaining the formation of the cave, and the 0.6-mile Wooded Trail winds along large sinkholes that connect to the cave system below.

FALLS OF THE OHIO
50
World-Class Fossil Beds in Limestone Ledges
38.2765, -85.7634

World famous for its fossil beds, the Falls of the Ohio are located along the banks of the Ohio River in Clark County. An expansive fossilized coral reef forms a low 1.5-mile-long island along the river's north shore across from Louisville, Kentucky. The reef is part of a limestone ridge that creates a 3-mile-long series of rapids, which gives the area its name. Ancient mastodons, mammoths, and bison crossed here on their way to salt licks in Kentucky, and Native Americans and early European explorers used the shallow waters as a passageway during low-flow stages. More than 600 species of fossils have been described from the prolific fossil beds, supporting the claim that more new species have been named from the Falls of the Ohio than any other locality in the world.

The Falls of the Ohio are located in the Charlestown Hills, a region composed of low-relief hills of Devonian- and Silurian-age strata bound sharply by the Knobstone Escarpment to the west. A northwest-trending anticline forms a ridge beneath the Ohio River at the Falls, and the oldest strata in this anticline were exposed through glacial erosion. During the middle of the Pleistocene Epoch, ice sheets from the Illinoian Stage of glaciation advanced to near the present position of the Ohio River and blocked preglacial drainage routes. Massive amounts of meltwater poured from the ice front, carving deep river valleys into the soft sedimentary bedrock. With each advance and retreat of the ice, the channels were scoured deeper and wider. Later during the Wisconsin Stage of glaciation, which did not reach Clark County, meltwater deposited a thick layer of outwash that buried the weathered valleys below. In the past 10,000 years, the Ohio River shifted to a position above the bedrock ridge, removing 60 to 70 feet of unconsolidated sediment and bedrock to expose the fossil beds seen today.

It is difficult to imagine the abundance of fossils at the Falls of the Ohio until you visit. The majority of the fossil beds are contained within the Middle Devonian Jeffersonville Limestone, a coarse-grained limestone that crops out in the exposed fossil beds. Millions of individual brachiopod, bryozoan, echinoderm, mollusk, trilobite, stromatoporoid sponge, and coral specimens are preserved in stunning detail in the water-polished bedding-plane exposures. The fossils can be divided

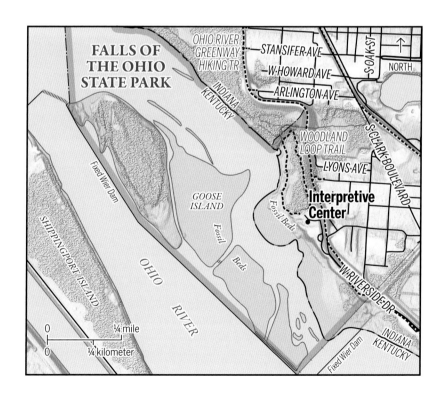

The limestone ridge that extends across the Ohio River was seasonally unnavigable by boat until the completion of the McAlpine Locks and Dam in 1830.

into five biozones, each having a unique collection of organisms that lived in specific areas of the Devonian reef. The youngest and highest strata, yellowish-brown limestone with abundant fenestrate bryozoans and brachiopods, are within the *Paraspirifer acuminatus* zone. Below this lies the Fenestrate Bryozoan-Brachiopod zone, which includes its namesakes as well as some corals. As you walk further down the fossil beds toward the shoreline, the fossils get older and larger. The *Brevispirifer gregarious* zone has brachiopods, large snails, and smaller corals. The *Amphipora ramosa* zone contains large mat-like stromatoporoid sponges, horn coral, and colonial coral, while the lowest Coralline zone contains the abundant corals for which the Falls are famed. One horn coral measures 4 feet in length, the largest found in North America. To visit, walk down the sidewalk from the Falls of the Ohio State Park's interpretive center and climb down the limestone ledges. Access to the fossil beds is best when the Ohio River is low and the lower coral zone is exposed. Be sure to bring a bucket or sponge to wet and clean the fossils to see them more clearly.

Several fossil specimens, such as this Thamnopora branching coral, were preserved through silicification, which produces a hardened black surface that weathers out of the limestone bedrock.

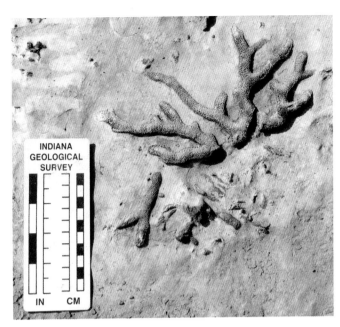

The upper fossil beds contain abundant fenestrate bryozoans and large spiriferid brachiopods. Overall, specimens get larger as you approach the river.

GLOSSARY

aggregate. Sand, gravel, or crushed rock mined for use as a construction material.

anticline. A ridge-shaped fold of rock, convex upward, whose core contains stratigraphically older rocks.

basin. A low area on the Earth's crust where sediments have accumulated.

bedding. The arrangement of a sedimentary rock in beds or layers of varying thickness and character; or the physical character or pattern of the beds, for example, cross-bedding or planar bedding.

bedrock. A general term for rock, usually solid, that underlies soil or other unconsolidated, surficial material.

bivalve (clam). A marine invertebrate animal with two-part shells that are symmetrical on the hinge line; a common fossil in Indiana rocks.

brachiopod. A marine invertebrate animal with two-part shells that have bilateral symmetry.

bryozoan. Aquatic invertebrate animals with colonial growth and a calcareous skeleton; one of the most common fossils in Indiana rocks.

calcite. A common rock-forming mineral composed of calcium carbonate.

carbonate bank. A ridgelike deposit made up of marine skeletal matter (for example, crinoids or brachiopods).

carbonate rock. A sedimentary rock, such as limestone or dolostone, composed of a majority of carbonate minerals.

cataract. Waterfall.

cave. Also known as **cavern**. A natural opening in the Earth formed by the dissolution of carbonate rock by weakly acidic water.

channel. A V- or U-shaped bed where a river or meltwater stream may flow. Channels in the glacial environment are commonly filled with sand and gravel deposited by meltwater.

chert. A hard, extremely dense sedimentary rock composed of microcrystalline quartz.

clastic. A type of rock made up of fragments (clasts) of other pre-existing minerals and rocks.

coarse-grained. Consisting of particles or grains that can be easily seen by the eye.

columnal. The stalk of a crinoid that is made up of cylindrical sections.

coral. Marine invertebrate animals with solitary or colonial growth and a calcareous skeleton; one of the most common fossils in Indiana rocks.

crinoid. A marine invertebrate animal characterized by feathery radiating arms, a cuplike head, and a stalk by which they attached to the seafloor; one of the most common fossils in Indiana rocks.

cross-bed. A sedimentary rock layer inclined at an angle to the main strata planes.

delta. A low, flat wedge of sediment deposited where a river or stream empties into a standing body of water.

depositional environment. The specific environment in which sediments are deposited, such as a stream channel, lake, or ocean bottom. Sometimes called **sedimentary environment**.

Devonian Period. Period of geologic time from about 416 to 359.2 million years ago.

dimension stone. A rock material that is quarried and cut into blocks or slabs for building.

dip. Refers to the angle at which bedrock strata are inclined from the horizontal.

dissolution. The dissolving of rock through chemical alteration.

dolomite. A rock-forming mineral composed of calcium carbonate and magnesium.

dolostone. A sedimentary rock composed primarily of dolomite that formed from the chemical alteration of limestone.

drapery. A cave feature usually composed of calcium carbonate that resembles the flowing drape of curtains.

dune. A hill or ridge of loose drifting sand that moves by wind action.

earthquake. A sudden motion or trembling of the Earth caused by the abrupt release of slowly accumulating strain.

echinoderm. A type of marine invertebrate animal that has a radiating arrangement of parts and a body characterized by protruding spines; includes the starfishes and sea urchins.

entrenched stream. A stream, often meandering, that flows in a narrow trench or valley cut into a plain or relatively level upland.

epoch. A geologic time unit that is longer than an age and shorter than a period.

erosion. The mechanical abrasion of material on the Earth's surface by glaciers, water, and wind.

erratic. A rock fragment that differs from the surrounding bedrock and was carried and deposited by glacial ice.

escarpment. A long cliff or steep slope that faces in one direction, breaking the continuity of the land by separating two level surfaces. It was produced by erosion or faulting.

esker. A long, narrow, often sinuous ridge of sand, gravel, or boulders deposited between ice walls by a stream flowing on or beneath a stagnant glacier.

fault. A break in rock layers along which there has been movement on one side relative to rock on the adjacent side.

fine-grained. Consisting of small particles or grains that are too small to see easily without magnification.

flowstone. A coating on the floor or wall of a cave consisting of a sheet of calcium carbonate deposited by slowly flowing water.

gastropod. A coiled-shell invertebrate animal; a common fossil in Indiana rocks.

geode. A cauliflower-shaped nodule that occurs in rocks that crop out throughout south-central Indiana; composed of quartz and calcite, many have hollow interiors containing various mineral crystals.

glacial drift. A general term for rock material and sediments transported by glaciers.

glacier. A mass of ice that flows under its own weight by internal deformation, basal sliding, or other mechanisms.

groundwater. All water present below the surface of the Earth.

Illinoian Stage. A period of major glacial activity that took place from 300,000 to 132,000 years ago. Deposits from this period are exposed at the modern land surface in southeastern and southwestern Indiana, beyond the limit of the Wisconsin ice sheets.

Illinois Basin. A relatively shallow structural basin that underlies southwestern Indiana, western Kentucky, and central and southern Illinois.

in situ. A Latin phrase meaning "in its original place."

interglacial. A period of milder climate between two glacial periods.

joint. A crack or fracture in a rock or sediment.

kame. A rounded hill or irregularly shaped mound of sand and gravel formed by streams flowing on or beneath a glacier.

karst. Topography typically formed on limestone, primarily by dissolution, and characterized by sinkholes, caves, and underground drainage. The topography of the Mitchell Plateau region of Indiana is mostly karst.

karst window. A sinkhole feature resulting from the collapse of a cave roof. In a karst window, a spring emerges and then abruptly disappears into the sinkhole.

kettle. A depression in the ground surface formed by the melting of a block of ice buried or partly buried by glacial drift.

klint (plural **klintar**). An exhumed fossil reef, its surrounding rocks having been eroded, leaving the reef core standing in relief as a knob, ridge, or hill.

Laurentide Ice Sheet. The continental-scale ice sheet that covered millions of square miles, including most of Canada and a large portion of the northern United States, multiple times 2.6 million to 12,000 years ago during the Pleistocene Epoch.

Liesegang rings. Nested rings or bands caused by rhythmic precipitation of iron oxides within a fluid-saturated rock.

limestone. A sedimentary rock composed primarily of calcite.

liquefaction. Ground failure or loss of strength, usually as a result of a moderate to severe earthquake, that causes otherwise solid soil to behave temporarily as a viscous liquid.

lobe (glacial). A tongue-like projection protruding from the mass of a continental glacier.

loess. Yellowish-gray deposit of windblown silt sediment.

meander. One of a series of sinuous bends, turns, or loops in the course of a stream.

meltwater. Water from the melting of glacial ice. It is typically discharged from the margin of an ice sheet or glacier, where it may occupy broad river channels that carry large amounts of sediment.

meteor impact feature. A crater or depression resulting from a meteor striking the surface of the Earth.

Mississippian culture. A mound-building Native American civilization that existed from approximately AD 800 to 1600. The term is not related to the Mississippian Period of geologic time.

Mississippian Period. Period of geologic time from about 359.2 to 318.1 million years ago.

moraine. Broad ridges of till deposited where the outer margin of glacial ice became stationary for a period of time.

mound (archaeology). A deliberately constructed earthen hill or earthwork.

oolitic limestone. A sedimentary rock composed of sand-sized spherical carbonate grains.

Ordovician Period. Period of geologic time from about 488.3 to 443.7 million years ago.

outcrop. The part of a geologic formation or structure that appears at the surface of the Earth.

outwash. Layered sand and gravel deposited by meltwater streams beyond glacial ice.

overlain. To lay over or upon, such as geologic strata.

Pennsylvanian Period. Period of geologic time from about 320 to 290 million years ago.

period. A fixed span of geologic time.

Pleistocene Epoch. Epoch of geologic time from about 2.6 million to 10,000 years ago.

Pre-Illinoian Stage. The oldest glacial stage in the Quaternary Period; it occurred approximately 2.5 million to 300,000 years ago.

quartz. A common rock-forming mineral composed of silica (silicon dioxide).

reef. A ridge or mound built by carbonate-secreting organisms such as corals at or near the surface of the sea.

Richmondian Invasion. An influx of species into the Cincinnati, Ohio, area during the Late Ordovician Period. They had evolved in previously isolated marine basins.

seismic. Relating to earthquakes or other vibrations in the Earth's crust.

shoal. A submerged bank or bar of unconsolidated material that rises from a body of water.

silicification. The process by which organic matter becomes saturated with silica.

Silurian Period. Period of geologic time from about 443.7 to 416 million years ago.

sinkhole. A depression in a karst area, commonly circular, that may be a few inches to several miles across. Its drainage is subterranean.

soda straw. A thin tubular stalactite that resembles a drinking straw.

spring. Any place where groundwater discharges onto the land surface because the water table intersects with the ground.

stalactite. Columnar deposits, usually of calcium carbonate, formed on the roof of a cave by the dripping of mineral solutions.

strata. Sheetlike layers of sedimentary rocks.

structural dome. A circular or elliptical feature formed by the upwarping of rock strata.

subterranean. Under the Earth's surface.

swallow hole. An opening or depression in the ground surface where a surface stream loses its water into the ground.

table rock. A flat-topped rock column, usually sedimentary rock, that is wider at the top due to erosion and weathering.

Teays River Valley. The valley of a preglacial river that drained much of the present Ohio River watershed.

texture. The relative proportions of particles of different sizes in a sediment deposit, such as pebbles, sand, silt, and clay.

till. That part of glacial drift that had little or no transportation or sorting by water; a mixture of clay, sand, gravel, and boulders.

till plain. An extensive flat to gently rolling area that is composed primarily of glacial till.

unconformity. A gap in the geologic record where a rock unit is overlain by another that is not next in stratigraphic succession; it is attributable to erosion or a period of nondeposition.

unconsolidated sediment. A sediment whose particles are not cemented together; unconsolidated sediments of Quaternary age are commonly referred to as glacial drift.

underlie. To be situated under; to occupy a position lower than.

weathering. The breakdown or decomposition of rock through mechanical, chemical, and organic processes.

whetstone. A hard, fine-grained stone that is used for a sharpening stone.

Wisconsin Stage. The most recent period of major glacial activity, from 79,000 to 10,000 years ago. Nearly the entire modern landscape of the northern two-thirds of Indiana, and a large part of the deposits beneath, are the products of this stage of the Pleistocene ice age.

REFERENCES

GENERAL SOURCES

Blatchley, W. S., ed. 1895. *Department of Geology and Natural Resources, Twelfth Annual Report.* Wm. B. Burford, Contractor for State Printing and Binding.

Camp, M. J., and Richardson, G. T. 1999. *Roadside Geology of Indiana.* Mountain Press.

Collett, J., ed. 1881. *Indiana Department of Geology and Natural History, Eleventh Annual Report.* WM. B. Burford, Contractor for State Printing and Binding.

Freeman, O. W. 1946. Geologic Contrasts in Indiana State Parks. *Proceedings of the Indiana Academy of Science* 55: 83–88.

Gray, H. H. 1989. *Quaternary Geologic Map of Indiana.* Indiana Geological Survey Miscellaneous Map 49.

——. 2000. *Physiographic Divisions of Indiana.* Indiana Geological Survey Special Report 61.

——. 2001. *Map of Indiana Showing Physiographic Divisions.* Indiana Geological Survey Miscellaneous Map 69.

Gray, H. H., Ault, C. H., and Keller, S. J. 1987. *Bedrock Geologic Map of Indiana.* Indiana Geological Survey Miscellaneous Map 48.

Jackson, M. T., ed. 1997. *The Natural Heritage of Indiana.* Indiana University Press.

Johnson, M. R., and Russell, K. P. 2015. *Indiana.* Indiana Geological Survey Miscellaneous Map 100.

Jordan, C. 2006. *The Nature Conservancy's Guide to Indiana Preserves.* Quarry Books, an imprint of Indiana University Press.

Leverett, F., and Taylor, F. B. 1915. *The Pleistocene of Indiana and Michigan and the History of the Great Lakes.* US Geological Survey Monograph 53.

Lindsey, A. A., ed. 1966. *Natural Features of Indiana: A Symposium Held April 22-23, 1966, at Wabash College, Crawfordsville, Indiana.* Indiana Academy of Science.

Lindsey, A. A., Schmelz, D. V., and Nichols S. A. 1970. *Natural Areas in Indiana and their Preservation.* Indiana Natural Areas Survey, Department of Biological Sciences, Purdue University.

Logan, W. N., Cummings, E. R., Malott, C. A., Visher, S. S., Tucker, W. M., and Reeves, J. R. 1922. *Handbook of Indiana Geology.* Indiana Department of Conservation.

McPherson, A. 1996. *Nature Walks in Northern Indiana.* Hoosier Chapter of the Sierra Club.

——. 2001. *Indiana's Best Hikes.* Waters Publishing Company.

——. 2002. *Nature Walks in Southern Indiana.* Waters Publishing Company.

Scholle, P. A., Bebout, D. G., and Moore, C. H., eds. 1983. *Carbonate Depositional Environments.* American Association of Petroleum Geologists Memoir 33.

Taylor, R. M., Jr., Stevens, E. W., Ponder, M. A., and Brockman, P. 1989. *Indiana: A New Historical Guide.* Indiana Historical Society.

Wayne, W. J. 1963. *Pleistocene Formations in Indiana.* Indiana Geological Survey Bulletin 25.

NORTHERN MORAINE AND LAKE REGION

1. INDIANA DUNES

Baedke, S. J., and Thompson, T. A. 2000. A 4,700-Year Record of Lake Level and Isostasy for Lake Michigan. *Journal of Great Lakes Research* 26 (4): 416–426.

Hill, J. R. 1973. *Geology for the Public: A Field Guide to the Lake Michigan Shore in Indiana.* Indiana Geological Survey Guidebook 2.

——. 1979. *Geologic Story of Indiana Dunes State Park.* Indiana Geological Survey State Park Guide 08.

——. 1974. *The Indiana Dunes-Legacy of Sand.* Indiana Geological Survey Special Report 8.

Thompson, T. A. n.d. *After the Thaw–The Development of Lake Michigan*. Indiana Geological Survey. https://igws.indiana.edu/FossilsAndTime/LakeMichigan.cfm#.

——. 1992. Beach-Ridge Development and Lake-Level Variation in Southern Lake Michigan. In *Research Conference on Quaternary Coastal Evolution*, Donoghue, J. F., Davis, R. A., Fletcher, C. H., and Suter, J. R., eds. *Sedimentary Geology* 80: 305–318.

Thompson, T. A., and Baedke, S. J. 1995. Beach-Ridge Development in Lake Michigan: Shoreline Behavior in Response to Quasi-Periodic Lake-Level Events. *Marine Geology* 129: 163–174.

Thompson, T. A., Baedke, S., Johnson, J. W., Sowder, K., and Hill, B. T. 2011. *Ancient Shorelines of Southwestern Lake Michigan*. Indiana Geological Survey Poster 2.1.

2. POKAGON STATE PARK

Bleuer, N. K. 1974. *Geologic Story of Pokagon State Park*. Indiana Geological Survey State Park Guide 1.

Sturgeon, P. R., Loope, H. M., and Russell, K. 2017. *Glacial Features of Indiana*. Indiana Geological and Water Survey Digital Information Series 14. https://igws.indiana.edu/IGSMap/GlacialFeatures.

3. CHAIN O'LAKES STATE PARK

Hill, J. R., and Ruppert, P. 1988. *Geologic Story of Chain O'Lakes State Park*. Indiana Geological Survey State Park Guide 10.

Swinehart, A. L., and Parker, G. R. 2002. The Relationship between Glacial Geologic Processes and Peatland Distribution in Indiana. *Proceedings of the Indiana Academy of Science* 1: 21–31.

4. KANKAKEE SANDS PRESERVE

Curry, B. B., Hajic, E. R., Clark, J. A., Befus, K. M., Carrell, J. E., and Brown, S. E. 2014. The Kankakee Torrent and Other Large Meltwater Flooding Events During the Last Deglaciation, Illinois, USA. *Quaternary Science Reviews* 90: 22–36.

Manes, J., Kallies, B., Desch, T., and Schreffler, L. 2012. *Everglades of the North: The Story of the Grand Kankakee Marsh*. Lakeshore Public Television.

5. FOX ISLAND COUNTY PARK

Bleuer, N. K., and Moore, M. C. 1972. Glacial Stratigraphy of the Fort Wayne, Indiana, Area and the Drainage of Glacial Lake Maumee. *Proceedings of the Indiana Academy of Science* 81: 195–209.

——. 1978. *Environmental Geology of Allen County*. Indiana Geological Survey Special Report 13.

Fleming, A. H. 1994. *The Hydrogeology of Allen County, Indiana: A Geologic and Ground-Water Atlas*. Indiana Geological Survey Special Report 57.

——. 2014. *Geology of the Little River Valley*. Little River Wetlands Project. http://www.lrwp.org/page/geology.

Sunderman, J. A. 1988. *Geology of Fox Island County Park*. Fox Island Alliance Nature Publication No. 5.

CENTRAL TILL PLAIN REGION

6. ARDMORE QUARRY

7. HANGING ROCK NATURE PRESERVE

8. BIG FOUR RAILROAD CUT

Ault, C. H. 1992. *Exposures of Silurian Reefs in Indiana*. Indiana Geological Survey Occasional Paper 61.

Cumings, E. R., and Shrock, R. R. 1928. *The Geology of the Silurian Rocks of Northern Indiana*. Indiana Department of Conservation Publications 75.

Cumings, E. R., and Shrock, R. R. 1928. Niagaran Coral Reefs of Indiana and Adjacent States and their Stratigraphic Relations. *Geological Society of America Bulletin* 39: 579–620.

Dickas, A. B. 2012. *101 American Geo-Sites You've Gotta See*. Mountain Press.

Droste, J. B., and Shaver, R. H. 1982. *The Salina Group (Middle and Upper Silurian) of Indiana*. Indiana Geological Survey Special Report 24.

Shaver, R. H. 1987. The Silurian Reefs near Wabash, Indiana. In *Geological Society of America Centennial Field Guide: North-Central Section*, v. 3: 333–336.

Wayne, W. J. 1968. *Geology Field Trip: Indiana Academy of Science, Wabash, Indiana, April 29, 1968*. Indiana Academy of Science.

9. SEVEN PILLARS OF THE MISSISSINEWA

Thornbury, W. D., and Deane, H. L. 1955. *The Geology of Miami County, Indiana*. Indiana Geological Survey Bulletin 8.

10. TIPPECANOE BATTLEFIELD

Bleuer, N. K. 1989. *Historical and Geomorphic Concepts of the Lafayette Bedrock Valley System (So-Called Teays Valley) in Indiana*. Indiana Geological Survey Special Report 46.

Edmunds, R. D. 1983. *The Shawnee Prophet*. University of Nebraska Press.

Feldman, J. 2005. *When the Mississippi Ran Backwards: Empire, Intrigue, Murder, and the New Madrid Earthquakes*. Free Press.

Sudgen, J. 1999. *Tecumseh: A Life*. Holt.

West, T. R., and Dagon, M. J. 2007. *Applied Geology in Tippecanoe County, Indiana: 8th Annual PGI All Universities Roaming Field Trip, Saturday, October 13, 2007*. Purdue University.

11. KENTLAND DOME

Gutschick, R. C. 1987. The Kentland Dome, Indiana: A Structural Anomaly. *Geological Society of America Centennial Field Guide: North-Central Section*, v. 3: 337–342.

Weber, J. C., Poulos, C., Donelick, R. A., Pope, M. C., and Heller, N. 2005. The Kentland Impact Crater, Indiana (USA): An Apatite Fission-Track Age Determination Attempt. In *Impact Tectonics*, Koeberl, C., and Henkel, H., eds. Springer: 447–466.

12. FALL CREEK GORGE

13. WILLIAMSPORT FALLS

Wayne, W. J., Johnson, G. H., and Keller, S. J. 1966. *Geologic Map of the 1 x 2 Danville Quadrangle, Indiana and Illinois Showing Bedrock and Unconsolidated Deposits*. Indiana Geological Survey Regional Geologic Map 2.

14. PORTLAND ARCH

Anuta, A. E., Jr. 1959. *Technical Rock Climbing at Portland Arch, Fountain, Indiana*. Purdue Outing Club, Purdue University.

Bieber, C. L. 1962. The Relation of Changing Facies of the Mansfield Formation to Possible Park Sites in Western Indiana. *Proceedings of the Indiana Academy of Science* 72: 177–181.

15. SUGAR CREEK TRAIL

Ausich, W. I. 1999. Lower Mississippian Edwardsville Formation at Crawfordsville, Indiana, US. In *Fossil Crinoids*, Hess, H., Ausich, W. I., Brett, C. E., and Simms, M. J., eds. Cambridge University Press: 145–154.

Ausich, W. I., Kammer, T. W., and Lane, N. G. 1979. Fossil Communities of the Borden (Mississippian) Delta in Indiana and Northern Kentucky. *Journal of Paleontology* 53 (5): 1,182–1,196.

Ausich, W. I., and Lane. N. G. 1982. Crinoids from the Edwardsville Formation (Lower Mississippian) of Southern Indiana. *Journal of Paleontology* 56 (6): 1,343–1,361.

Ausich, W. I., and Webster, G. D., eds. 2008. *Echinoderm Paleobiology*. Indiana University Press.

Morgan, W. W. 2014. *Collector's Guide to Crawfordsville Crinoids*. Schiffer Publishing.

16. TURKEY RUN STATE PARK

17. SHADES STATE PARK

Bridges, K. H. P. 1977. *Geologic Story of Shades State Park*. Indiana Geological Survey State Park Guide 4.

Bridges, K. H. P. 1977. *Geologic Story of Turkey Run State Park*. Indiana Geological Survey State Park Guide 5.

Burger, A. M., Rexroad, C. B., Schneider, A. F., and Shaver, R. H. 1966. *Excursions in Indiana Geology*. Indiana Geological Survey Guidebook 12: 49–51.

Esarey, R. E., Bieberman, D. F., and Bieberman, R. A. 1950. *Stratigraphy along the Mississippian-Pennsylvanian Unconformity of Western Indiana*. Indiana Geological Survey Guidebook 4.

Kvale, E. P., Fishbaugh, D., and Archer, A. 2016. *Association of Tidal and Fluvial Sediments within the Mansfield Formation (Pennsylvanian), Turkey Run State Park, Parke County, Indiana*. Indiana Geological Survey Field Trip Guidebook 17.

Weir, C. E., and Wayne, W. J. 1953. *An Introduction to the Geology of Parke County, Indiana*. Indiana Geological Survey Circular 2.

18. INDIANA STATE MUSEUM

Carmony, D. F. 1968. The New Indiana State Museum. *Indiana Magazine of History* 64: 191–208.

Kimberling, C. 1996. David Dale Owen and Joseph Graville Norwood: Pioneer Geologists in Indiana and Illinois. *Indiana Magazine of History* 92: 1–25.

Lane, N. G. 2000. *Geology at Indiana University, 1840–2000*. Indiana University Department of Geological Sciences.

19. TRENTON FIELD

Rarick, R. D. 1980. *The Petroleum Industry: Its Birth in Pennsylvania and Development in Indiana*. Indiana Geological Survey Occasional Paper 32.

Sullivan, D. M. 1995. *Natural Gas Fields of Indiana*. Indiana Geological Survey Special Report 51.

20. WHITEWATER VALLEY GORGE PARK

21. BROOKVILLE LAKE DAM

Dattilo, B. F. 2015. *Field Trip #1–Stratigraphy and Sedimentology of the Upper Ordovician in Southeastern Indiana*. Self-published.

Dattilo, B. F., Aucoin, C. D., Brett, C. E., and Schramm, T. J. 2013. *Fossils and Stratigraphy of the Upper Ordovician Standard in South Eastern Indiana*. Self-published.

Davis, R. A., ed. 1961. *Cincinnati Fossils: An Elementary Guide to the Ordovician Rocks and Fossils of the Cincinnati, Ohio, Region*. Cincinnati Museum of Natural History.

Holland, S. M., Davis, R. A., and Meyer, D. L. 2009. *A Sea without Fish: Life in the Ordovician Seas of the Cincinnati Region*. Indiana University Press.

McLaughlin, P. I., Brett, E. W., Holland, S. M., and Storrs, G. W., eds. 2008. *Stratigraphic Renaissance in the Cincinnati Arch: Implications for Upper Ordovician Paleontology and Paleoecology*. Cincinnati Museum Center.

Stigall, A. L. 2018. *The Digital Atlas of Ordovician Life: Exploring the Fauna of the Cincinnati Region*. http://www.ordovicianatlas.org/.

22. ANDERSON FALLS

Hasenmueller, W. A., Rupp, R. F., Johnson, M. R., and Armstrong, I. P. 2017. *The Bedrock Geology of Bartholomew County*. Indiana Geological and Water Survey Digital Information 16. https://igws.indiana.edu/IGSMap/BartholomewCounty.

SOUTHERN HILLS AND LOWLANDS REGION

23. FLATWOODS PARK

Malott, C. A., and Gray, H. H. 1979. *The Flatwoods Region of Owen and Monroe Counties, Indiana*. Indiana Geological Survey Occasional Paper 28.

24. MCCORMICK'S CREEK STATE PARK

Gray, H. H. 1977. *Geologic Story of McCormick's Creek State Park*. Indiana Geological Survey State Park Guide 3.

Gray, H. H., Bleuer, N., Hill, J., and Linebeck, J. 1979. *Geologic Map of the 1 x 2 Indianapolis Quadrangle, Indiana and Illinois, Showing Bedrock and Unconsolidated Deposits*. Indiana Geological Survey Regional Geologic Map 1.

25. CEDAR BLUFFS NATURE PRESERVE

Hartke, E. J., and Gray, H. H. 1989. *Geology for Environmental Planning in Monroe County, Indiana*. Indiana Geological Survey Special Report 47.

Hasenmueller, W. A., Estell, C. M., Keith, B., and Thompson, T. A. 2009. *Bedrock Geologic Map of Monroe County, Indiana*. Indiana Geological Survey Miscellaneous Map 73.

26. MONROE LAKE

Ausich, W. I., Kammer, T. W., and Lane, N. G. 1979. Fossil Communities of the Borden (Mississippian) Delta in Indiana and Northern Kentucky. *Journal of Paleontology* 53 (5): 1,182–1,196.

Ausich, W. I., and Lane, N. G. 1980. Field Trip 2: Platform Communities and Rocks of the Borden Siltstone Delta (Mississippian) along the South Shore of Monroe Reservoir, Monroe County, Indiana. In *Field Trips 1980 from the Indiana University Campus, Bloomington, North-Central Section of the Geological Society of America*, Shaver, R. H., ed.: 36–67.

Ausich, W. I., and Lane. N. G. 1982. Crinoids from the Edwardsville Formation (Lower Mississippian) of Southern Indiana. *Journal of Paleontology* 56 (6): 1,343–1,361.

Kammer, T. W., Ausich, W. I., and Lane, N. G. 1983. Paleontology and Stratigraphy of the Borden Delta of Southern Indiana and Northern Kentucky (Field Trip 2). In *Field Trips in Midwestern Geology*. Annual Meeting of the Geological Society of America, v. 1, Shaver, R. H., and Sunderman, J. A., eds.: 37–71.

27. INDIANA UNIVERSITY CAMPUS

28. LAND OF LIMESTONE MUSEUM

Bell, R. 2008. *Early History of Indiana Limestone*. AuthorHouse.

Blatchley, R. S. 1907. *The Indiana Oolitic Limestone Industry in 1907*. Contractor for State Printing and Binding: 301–459.

Keith, B. D. 2005. *A Walking Tour of Building Stone and Architecture on the Bloomington Campus of Indiana University*. Indiana Geological Survey Open-File Study 04-06.

McDonald, B. 1995. *A Short History of Indiana Limestone*. Bedford, Indiana.

Patton, J. B., and Carr, D. D. 1982. *The Salem Limestone in the Indiana Building-Stone District*. Indiana Geological Survey Occasional Paper 38.

Rooney, L. F. 1970. *Dimension Limestone Resources of Indiana*. Indiana Geological Survey Bulletin 42C.

Stuckey, C. W. 1989. *Early Quarries of Owen & Monroe Counties 1850–1907*. Self-published.

——. 1989. *Gazetteer of Limestone Mills of Owen, Monroe, and Lawrence Counties to 1950*. Self-published.

Sturgeon, P. R., and Johnson, M. R. 2017. *Indiana Limestone*. Indiana Geological and Water Survey Digital Information 12. https://igws.indiana.edu/IGSMap/IndianaLimestone.

Thompson, T. A. 1990. *Architectural Elements and Paleoecology of Carbonate Shoal and Intershoal Deposits in the Salem Limestone (Mississippian) in South-Central Indiana*. Indiana Geological Survey Guidebook 14.

29. MOUNT CARMEL FAULT

Keller, S. J. 1998. *Underground Storage of Natural Gas in Indiana*. Indiana Geological Survey Special Report 59.

Melhorn, W. N., and Smith, N. M. 1959. *The Mt. Carmel Fault and Related Structural Features in South-Central Indiana*. Indiana Geological Survey Report of Progress 16.

Shaver, R. H., and Austin, G. S. 1972. *A Field Guide to the Mt. Carmel Fault of Southern Indiana*. Indiana Geological Survey Guidebook 13.

30. CATARACT FALLS

Conner, G. A. 1986. Type Section for Indian Creek Limestone Beds in the Ste. Genevieve Formation of South Central Indiana. *Proceedings of the Indiana Academy of Science* 95: 307–311.

Malott, C. A. 1946. The Geology of Cataract Falls, Owen County, Indiana. *The Journal of Geology* 54 (5): 322–326.

McGrain, P. 1948. Geological Features of the Proposed Cagle's Mill Flood Control Reservoir. *Proceedings of the Indiana Academy of Science* 58: 163–172.

Thornbury, W. D. 1940. Glacial Lakes Quincy and Eminence. *Proceedings of the Indiana Academy of Science* 49: 131–144.

31. CAGLES MILL SPILLWAY

Burger, A. M, Rexroad, C. B., Schneider, A. F., and Shaver, R. H. 1966. *Excursions in Indiana Geology*. Indiana Geological Survey Guidebook 12: 43–46.

Hasenmueller, W. A., and Bleuer, N. K. 1987. Cataract Lake Emergency Spillway, Southwestern Indiana. In *Geological Society of America Centennial Field Guide: North-Central Section*, v. 3: 349–353.

Hill, J. R., Moore, M. C., and Mackey, J. C. 1982. *Bedrock Geology and Mineral Resources of Putnam County Indiana*. Indiana Geological Survey Special Report 26.

Schneider, A. F., and Wayne, W. J. 1967. Field Trip No. 3, Pleistocene Stratigraphy of West-Central Indiana. In *Geologic Tales along Hoosier Trails: A Field Trip Guidebook Prepared for the First Annual Meeting of the North-Central Section of the Geological Society of America*, Schneider, A. F., ed.: 77–103.

32. BROWN COUNTY STATE PARK

Collett, J. 1875. Geology of Brown County. In *Sixth Annual Report of the Geological Survey of Indiana*. Sentinel Company: 77–110.

Hill, J. R. 1981. *Geologic Story of Brown County State Park*. Indiana Geological Survey State Park Guide 9.

Sowder, K. H., and Irwin, P. 2008. *Shaded Relief Map of Brown County, Indiana*. Indiana Geological Survey Shaded Relief Topographic Map 7.

33. KNOBSTONE ESCARPMENT

Payne, J. 1981. Knobstone Trail Reflections. In *Outdoor Indiana*. April issue: 4–9.

Strange, N. D. 2011. *A Guide to the Knobstone Trail: Indiana's Longest Footpath*. Indiana University Press.

34. TUNNEL MILL

35. MUSCATATUCK COUNTY PARK

Esarey, R. E., Malott, C. A., and Galloway, J. J. 1947. *Silurian and Devonian Formations in Southeastern Indiana*. Indiana Geological Survey Field Conference Guidebook 1.

Jennings County Historical Society. 2005. *Jennings County Indiana, 1816–1999*. Jennings County Historical Society.

36. VERSAILLES STATE PARK

Davis, R. A., ed. 1961. *Cincinnati Fossils: An Elementary Guide to the Ordovician Rocks and Fossils of the Cincinnati, Ohio, Region*. Cincinnati Museum of Natural History.

McLaughlin, P. I., Brett, E. W., Holland, S. M., and Storrs, G. W., eds. 2008. *Stratigraphic Renaissance in the Cincinnati Arch: Implications for Upper Ordovician Paleontology and Paleoecology*. Cincinnati Museum Center.

Rexroad, C. B. 1977. *Geologic Story of Versailles State Park*. Indiana Geological Survey State Park Guide 6.

Stigall, A. L. 2018. *The Digital Atlas of Ordovician Life, Exploring the Fauna of the Cincinnati Region*. http://www.ordovicianatlas.org/.

37. CLIFTY FALLS STATE PARK

Esarey, R. E., Malott, C. A., and Galloway, J. J. 1947. *Silurian and Devonian Formations in Southeastern Indiana*. Indiana Geological Survey Field Conference Guidebook 1.

Rexroad, C. B. 1975. *Geologic Story of Clifty Falls State Park*. Indiana Geological Survey State Park Guide 2.

Rexroad, C. B., and Orr, R. W. 1967. Field Trip No. 2, Silurian and Devonian Stratigraphy of Southeastern Indiana. In *Geologic Tales along Hoosier Trails: A Field Trip Guidebook Prepared for the First Annual Meeting of the North-Central Section of The Geological Society of America*, Schneider, A. F., ed.: 41–74.

Totten, S. M., and Hay, H. B. 1987. Madison, Indiana: Geomorphology, and Paleozoic and Quaternary Geology. In *Geological Society of America Centennial Field Guide: North-Central Section*, v. 3: 365–370.

38. JUG ROCK NATURE PRESERVE

Gray, H. H. 1962. *Outcrop Features of the Mansfield Formation in Southwestern Indiana*. Indiana Geological Survey Report of Progress 26.

39. HINDOSTAN FALLS

Bajza, C. C. 1944. *A Special Case of Circumvallation at Hindostan Falls Region, Martin County, Indiana*. Thesis (A.M.) Indiana University: 33.

Gray, H. H. 2001. Subglacial Meltwater Channels (Nye Channels or N-Channels) in Sandstone at Hindostan Falls, Martin County, Indiana. *Proceedings of the Indiana Academy of Science* 110: 1–8.

40. CROWN HILL CEMETERY

Hannibal, J. T. 2007. Teaching with Tombstones: Geology at the Cemetery. In *Proceedings of the 40th Forum on the Geology of Industrial Minerals (May 2–7, 2004, Bloomington, Indiana)*, Indiana Geological Survey Occasional Paper 67, Schaffer, N. R., and DeChurch, D. A., eds.: 82–88.

Kvale, E. P., and Powell, R. L. 2004. *Hindostan Whetstone Tombstone Industry in Indiana, 1811–1680*. Indiana Geological Survey.

———. 2009. *Indiana Whetstone Posters*. Indiana Geological Survey Open-File Study 09-03.

Kvale, E. P., Powell, R. L., and McNerney, M. J. 2000. The Art, History, and Geoscience of Hindostan Whetstone Gravestones in Indiana. *Journal of Geoscience Education* 48: 3.

41. SPRING MILL STATE PARK

42. LOST RIVER

43. WESLEY CHAPEL GULF AND ORANGEVILLE RISE

Florea, L. J., and Frushour, S. S. 2015. *Cave and Karst Hydrology: A Field Trip through Owen, Monroe, and Lawrence Counties, Indiana*. Indiana Geological Survey Field Trip Guidebook 16.

Frushour, S. S. 2012. *A Guide to Caves and Karst of Indiana*. Indiana University Press.

Hasenmueller, N. R., Rexroad, C. B., Powell, R. L., Buehler, M. A., and Bassett, J. L. 2003. *Karst Geology and Hydrology of the Spring Mill Lake and Lost River Drainage Basins in Southern Indiana*. Indiana Geological Survey Guidebook 15.

Keith, B. D., Thompson, T. A., Herrmann, E. W., Rupp, R. F., and Hasenmueller, W. A. 2014. *Geologic Map of Lawrence County, Indiana*. Indiana Geological Survey Miscellaneous Map 90.

Powell, R. L., and Thornbury, W. D. 1967. Field Trip No. 1: Karst Geomorphology of South-Central Indiana. In *Geologic Tales along Hoosier Trails: A Field Trip Guidebook Prepared for the First Annual Meeting of the North-Central Section of the Geological Society of America*, Schneider, A. F., ed.: 11–38.

Rexroad, C. B., and Gray, L. M. 1979. *Geologic Story of Spring Mill State Park*. Indiana Geological Survey State Park Guide 7.

44. WEBER LAKE

Coal Mine Information System. n.d. Indiana Department of Natural Resources. https://www.in.gov/dnr/reclamation/9310.htm.

Comer, J. B., ed. 2012. *Effects of Abandoned Mine Land Reclamation on Ground and Surface Water Quality: Research and Case Histories from Indiana*. Indiana Geological Survey Special Report 72.

45. ANGEL MOUNDS STATE HISTORIC SITE

Black, G. A. 1967. *Angel Site: An Archaeological, Historical, and Ethnological Study*. Indiana Historical Society.

Counts, R. C., Monaghan, W. G., Wilson, J. J., and Herrmann, E. 2013. *Liquefaction within Mound F at Angel Mounds: Evidence for Late Holocene Seismicity in the Midcontinental USA from an Archaeological Site, Southwestern Indiana*. Geological Society of America Annual Meeting 45.

Gray, W. E., Parke, M., and Steinmetz, J. C. 2012, *Map of Indiana Showing Liquefaction Potential of Surficial Materials*. Indiana Geological Survey Miscellaneous Map 86.

Gray, W. E., and Steinmetz, J. C. 2012. *Map of Indiana Showing Known Faults and Historic Earthquake Epicenters Having Magnitude of 3.0 and Larger*. Indiana Geological Survey Miscellaneous Map 84.

Jones, J. R., and Johnson, A. L. 1999. *Early Peoples of Indiana*. Division of History Preservation and Archaeology.

Monaghan, W. G., Schilling, T., Krus, A. M., and Peebles, C. S. 2014. Mound Construction Chronology at Angel Mounds Episodic Mound

Construction and Ceremonial Events. *Midcontinental Journal of Archaeology* 38 (2): 155–170.

Munson, P. J., Obermeier, S. F., Munson, C. A., and Hajic, E. R. 1997. Liquefaction Evidence for Holocene and Latest Pleistocene Seismicity in the Southern Halves of Indiana and Illinois: A Preliminary Overview. *Seismological Research Letter* 68 (4): 521–536.

46. NEW HARMONY

Elliott W. S., Jr. 2016. Crossroad of Art, Education, and Geology in New Harmony, Indiana: A New Exhibit at the Working Men's Institute. *Proceedings of the Indiana Academy of Science* 125 (1): 19–31.

Hendrickson, W. B. 1943. *David Dale Owen: Pioneer Geologist of the Middle West*. Indiana Historical Bureau.

Pitzer, D. E. 1989. The Original Boatload of Knowledge Down the Ohio River: William Maclure's and Robert Owen's Transfer of Science and Education to the Midwest, 1825–1826. *Ohio Journal of Science* 89 (5): 128–142.

Shaver, R. H. 1979. *Geologic Story of the Lower Wabash Valley with Emphasis on the New Harmony Area*. Indiana Geological Survey Occasional Paper 27.

Straw, W. T., and Doss, P. K. 2008. David Dale Owen and the Geological Enterprise of New Harmony, Indiana, with a Companion Roadside Geology of Vanderburgh and Posey Counties. In *From the Cincinnati Arch to the Illinois Basin: Geological Field Excursions along the Ohio River Valley*, Geological Society of America Field Guide 12, Maria, A. H., and Counts, R. C., eds.: 105–117.

Thomas, S. F., and Hannibal, J. T. 2008. Revisiting New Harmony in the Footsteps of Maximilian, the Prince of Wied; David Dale Owen; Charles Lesueur; and Other Early Naturalists. In *From the Cincinnati Arch to the Illinois Basin: Geological Field Excursions along the Ohio River Valley*, Geological Society of America Field Guide 12, Maria, A. H., and Counts, R. C., eds.: 25–45.

47. WYANDOTTE CAVES

Atz, A., ed. 2007. *Back Underground in Indiana: A Guidebook for the 2007 National Convention of the National Speleological Society*. National Speleological Society.

Frushour, S. S. 2007. The Geology of Wyandotte Cave. In *Back Underground in Indiana: A Guidebook for the 2007 National Convention of the National Speleological Society*, National Speleological Society, Atz, A., ed.: 186–194.

Indiana Geological and Water Survey. 2018. *The Wyandotte Caves Complex Including Easter Pit Cave*. Indiana Geological and Water Survey Miscellaneous Map 111.

Powell, R. L. 1968. The Geology and Geomorphology of Wyandotte Cave, Crawford County, Indiana. *Proceedings of the Indiana Academy of Science* 77: 236–244.

Powell, R. L. 2007. Projected Passage Profiles for the Wyandotte, Easter Pit, and Everton Caves System. In *Back Underground in Indiana: A Guidebook for the 2007 National Convention of the National Speleological Society*, National Speleological Society, Atz, A., ed.: 195–196.

48. BLUESPRING CAVERNS

Frushour, S. S. 2012. *A Guide to Caves and Karst of Indiana*. Indiana University Press.

49. INDIANA CAVERNS

Roberson, G. 2015. *The Geology of Indiana Caverns and the Binkley Cave System*. Indiana Caverns.

50. FALLS OF THE OHIO

Greb, S. F., Hendricks, R. T., and Chesnut, D. R., Jr. 1993. *Fossil Beds of the Falls of the Ohio*. Kentucky Geological Survey Special Publication 10.

Hendricks, R. T., Ettensohn, F. R., Stark, T. J., and Greb, S. F. 1994. *Geology of the Devonian Strata of the Falls of the Ohio Area, Kentucky-Indiana: Stratigraphy, Sedimentology, Paleontology, Structure, and Diagenesis*. Kentucky Geological Survey.

Powell, R. L. 1999. *Geology of the Falls of the Ohio River*. Indiana Geological Survey Circular 10.

Rexroad, C. B., and Powell, R. L. 1987. The Falls of the Ohio River, Indiana and Kentucky. In *Geological Society of America Centennial Field Guide: North-Central Section*, v. 3: 381–386.

Stumm, E. C. 1964. *Silurian and Devonian Corals of the Falls of the Ohio*. Geological Society of America.

INDEX

A dedicated group of geologists, cartographers, photographers, and editors at the Indiana Geological and Water Survey contributed to this book, the sixth in the state-by-state Geology Rocks! series. Left to right: John Day (photography), Matt Johnson (cartography), Barbara Hill (photography), Polly Sturgeon (text), Deborah DeChurch (editing), Todd Thompson (introduction).

ABOUT THE AUTHOR

The **Indiana Geological and Water Survey** (IGWS) is a research institute of Indiana University. Its mission is to provide geologic information and counsel that contribute to the wise stewardship of the energy, mineral, and water resources of the state. Since 1837, the health, safety, and welfare of Indiana's citizenry have benefited from a combination of IGWS activities: focused research initiatives and cooperative investigations with governmental agencies, businesses and industries, and educational organizations; geologic sample and data collection and archiving; and dissemination of information in many forms, including published maps, reports, databases, and educational outreach programs.

Polly Root Sturgeon is a geologist and educator with a specialty in interpreting earth science for the general public. As the Education Outreach Coordinator at the Indiana Geological and Water Survey, she invites enthusiasts young and old to explore the geological foundations of the place they call home. After earning a BS in history and geology from Olivet Nazarene University (2009) and an MS in geoscience education from Indiana University (2012), Polly joined the staff of the IGWS in 2015.